'Miss Waring, I'm desperate. You're my last hope.'

Sheila looked away, biting her lip. Her heart went out to the man, and, considering that it was her own husband who'd killed his wife and crippled his daughter, in a way she owed it to him to help him. But how could she stay in his house, knowing who he was? Wouldn't it be deception? And what if he discovered her real identity?

Dear Reader

Here we are once again at the end of the year...looking forward to Christmas and to the delightful surprises the new year holds. During the festivities, though, make sure you let Mills & Boon help you to enjoy a few precious hours of escape. For, with our latest selection of books, you can meet the men of your dreams and travel to far-away places—without leaving the comfort of your own fireside!

Till next month,

The Editor

Rosemary Hammond grew up in California, but has since lived in several other states. Rosemary and her husband have travelled extensively throughout the United States, Mexico, the Caribbean and Canada, both with and without their two sons. She enjoys gardening, music and needlework, but her greatest pleasure has always been reading. She started writing romances because she enjoyed them, but also because the mechanics of fiction fascinated her and she thought they might be something she could do.

Recent titles by the same author:

THE POWER OF LOVE
VOYAGE TO ENCHANTMENT

tone of her letter she sounds like a person who wouldn't be satisfied with anything less than a miracle.'

'True,' Kate agreed. 'But if you read carefully between the lines you can sense the desperation in her. Anyway, do you want to give it a try?'

Sheila hesitated, thinking it over. 'I'm not sure. I notice she expects the therapist to live in her house for however long it takes to get the girl on her feet. That could be weeks, even months. I don't know that I want to commit myself to such a long-term situation.'

Kate gave her a knowing smile. 'What is it? Don't you want to be away from David that long? Afraid some other woman might grab him if you're not there to protect your interests?'

Sheila stared at her, wide-eyed. 'Not at all. What makes you think that? In fact, there are times I wish he *would* find someone else, someone who really appreciated him.'

'And you don't?'

'Of course I do,' Sheila assured her hurriedly. 'He's a wonderful man, a fine doctor. If it hadn't been for him I might still be lying in a hospital bed. And you, too, Kate, of course. I owe everything to the two of you.'

Kate reddened. 'Oh, bosh! We were just doing our jobs. But I simply can't understand why you don't snap him up. He's obviously in love with you, has been from the start.'

'Oh, Kate, I can't explain. When Richard died, something in me seemed to have died with him. Don't think I'm not grateful for all you've done,' she added quickly. 'Helping me get back on my feet, giving me a job when I needed it most.'

'But you're still grieving for your husband, is that it?'

Sheila frowned. 'No. Not exactly. I mean, I think I've accepted the loss. Life does go on, and I'm content with mine just the way it is. I love my work, and I'm very glad to have a friend like David. I wish I could love him, but that's a part of me that seems to be over.' She smiled. 'Make any sense?'

'Not really,' Kate said, heaving her bulk up out of the chair. 'But it's your life, kiddo. So long as you're happy with it, who am I to judge? Now, what shall I tell Mrs Meredith? Actually, it wouldn't hurt to take a drive down to Monterey just to meet the child, make a preliminary prognosis, talk to the aunt.'

'No,' Sheila replied slowly. 'I guess I could do that.'

'Well, why not go this afternoon?' She glanced down at the appointment calendar on her desk. 'I could get Annabel to take your afternoon sessions if you like.'

'All right,' Sheila replied at last. 'I might as well. But it doesn't sound promising.'

By afternoon the fog had lifted. Kate had called ahead and made a two o'clock appointment with Mrs Meredith, and right after a quick lunch Sheila set out on the drive south along the coast highway that wound around the rocky cliffs high above the ocean. It was almost a two-hour drive from San Francisco to Monterey, but the day was fine, the road virtually deserted at this hour, and she was in no hurry.

As she drove she mulled over that morning's conversation with Kate. It had raised some issues she only wanted to forget, issues she thought she *had* forgotten. Now, however, driving along in the sunshine on the nearly empty road, the whole painful scenario flashed through her mind, and she was transported back in time, just about a year ago, when she'd woken up in a hospital bed, drifting slowly up into numbed consciousness.

Her first impression had been of a glaring whiteness, and, as she'd turned towards the light, immediately a tearing pain had shot from the top of her head down through the back of her neck, then settled in the middle of her spine, insistent, throbbing viciously. Instinctively she'd cried out, and in a moment she'd heard voices, a woman and a man.

'Good,' said the man. 'She's finally conscious. Better give her a stiff hypo now, Nurse. She needs to be kept in homeostasis for a while longer.'

'Yes, Doctor,' said the woman.

Doctor. Nurse. The whiteness. She must be in a hospital. She opened her mouth to speak, but nothing came out. The least attempt to move only revived the pain. All she could do was lie there, helpless, mute, immobile.

She felt something wet and cold on her upper arm, then a slight stinging sensation, and as the pain receded her eyes grew heavy again. Just before sinking back into oblivion, a sudden vivid image leapt into her mind—the rain-swept highway, the car swerving, the glare of oncoming headlights, the terrible crunching sound of metal on metal, then nothingness.

The next time she awoke her head seemed clearer and there was less pain. Someone was sitting beside her bed, leaning over her, a man wearing a white coat. The doctor.

'Where am I?' she mumbled groggily.

'Good,' came his pleased voice. 'You're awake. How do you feel? Any pain?'

'No, not as bad anyway.' She tried to sit up, but seemed to be held down by a heavy weight. 'Where am I?' she said again. 'What happened to me?'

'You've been in an automobile accident,' came the voice. 'You were badly injured, but you're going to be all right. How much do you remember?'

She thought a moment. 'I do recall the accident, but nothing after that. It's all a blank.'

'Well, that's only natural. You've been unconscious.'

'For how long?'

'Several days.'

'How badly am I hurt?'

'Well, your right hip was broken, you suffered a concussion, some lacerations on your legs and face, but no internal injuries. You're going to be fine, as good as new in no time.'

Then it hit her. 'Richard?' she asked. 'What about Richard?'

There was a long silence. 'I'm sorry, Mrs Fulton,' he said at last, his voice grave. 'Your husband didn't make it. We did everything we could for him, but the main impact was on the driver's side, and he never had a chance. I'm sorry.'

Dead? Richard dead? How could that be? She remembered the party at the Bennetts', Richard insisting on driving even though he'd had far too much to drink, then the crash. But how could he be gone like that? One minute vital and alive, the next simply vanished.

'What about the people in the other car?' she asked.

'I don't want you to worry about that now,' the doctor said in a firm voice. He rose to his feet. 'I'm going to give you something to make you sleep. You're mending nicely, but what you need most of all is rest, give the body a chance to heal itself.'

Once again, she felt the prick of the needle, then a slow drifting into unconsciousness.

After that the days passed by in a blur. She couldn't even begin to keep track of them, could only measure them by her slow but steady improvement. Gradually her strength began to come back. The hardest part of those long, half-unconscious days was coming to terms with Richard's death. They'd been married such a short time, less than a year, and she could still hardly grasp the fact that he was gone.

In time, her bodily functions returned to normal, and all the constricting tubes were removed. She was soon sitting up and eating the tasteless hospital meals on her own, even though she hadn't much appetite. Her face was still heavily bandaged, but by now she was well enough to be wheeled into the sun-room twice a day.

Although the nurses and doctors were kind and encouraging, they were all evasive about the people in the other car. David Fleming, the young doctor who had performed the surgery on her face, was especially friendly, and one day when he was putting on a new swath of bandages, bending over her, she tackled him again.

'That looks fine, Sheila,' he said with a smile. 'You'll have some scarring, but that lovely head of auburn hair will cover the worst of it for now, and they'll fade in time.'

'Dr Fleming,' she said firmly. 'No one will tell me about the people in the other car. Nothing you tell me could be worse than not knowing. Please. I'll have to find out sooner or later.'

The smile faded and he sighed. 'All right. You have a point. The driver came out of it unscathed, but there were serious injuries to the two passengers.'

'How serious?'

'It's too soon to tell,' he replied evasively. 'In any event, it's nothing for you to be concerned about or feel guilty over. You weren't driving after all. And not only do you have your own loss to deal with, you need all your strength to recuperate.'

She sank back on the pillows and closed her eyes. 'Yes,' she agreed. 'All right. Thank you for telling me.'

He remained standing there, hesitating, for a few moments, then reached down and gave her shoulder a gentle squeeze. 'Your business is to get well, Sheila. Just concentrate on that.'

But, as David and Kate kept reminding her, that was all in the past, months ago, and she must not dwell on it. Especially now, she suddenly realised, when she was driving along an unfamiliar road.

However, the directions Kate had given her were quite clear. The Meredith house was set high on a bluff overlooking the ocean, some five miles south of Monterey, and she was just approaching a crossroads where it was time to turn off the main highway.

She took a right and headed down a narrow road that wound around the rocky cliff until she came to a wrought-iron gate, standing open. She turned in, and before long reached an imposing house, low and sprawling, built of redwood siding and with a commanding view of the Pacific. The garden was a lush green of lawn, patches of Irish moss and low-growing shrubbery, with brightly blooming azaleas and rhododendrons interspersed among them.

She got out of the car and walked up the flagstone path to a pair of heavy carved oak doors. She rang the bell and in a moment it opened to reveal a tall, rather heavy-set woman of indeterminate age standing on the other side.

'You must be Sheila Waring,' she said with a smile. 'The therapist. Please come in.' She opened the door wider, and Sheila stepped inside into a wide hallway, paved in colourful glazed tile. 'I'm Jane Meredith,' the woman went on. 'And I can't tell you how glad I am to see you. I've been here for several weeks trying to help Ross with Beth until he could find someone capable of handling the girl, and I admit I'm at my wits' end.' She laughed. 'Not a very auspicious introduction to the job, is it? Please excuse my rambling on. Would you like to freshen up before I take you to meet him?'

'No,' Sheila murmured, somewhat nonplussed by the woman's overwhelming personality. 'I'm fine.'

'All right, just follow me,' she said, striding off down the hall. 'Ross is in his study.'

Sheila followed along, wondering who in the world this Ross was she kept talking about, but not liking to ask at this point. Her husband, most likely.

They soon came to another carved oak door. Jane Meredith gave one brisk knock, then opened it and ushered Sheila inside. A man was sitting at the desk by the window, his dark head bent over a stack of file folders, the sun shining on him in just such a way that she couldn't quite make out his features.

'Ross,' Jane Meredith said, 'this is Miss Waring, the therapist for Beth.' She turned to Sheila. 'Or is it Mrs? Or perhaps you prefer Ms?'

'Sheila will be fine,' she said with a smile, and gave the man at the desk an expectant look.

But when he raised his head, the smile died on her lips. The sudden shock was so overwhelming that for a moment she was afraid she'd faint dead away on the spot. It was all she could do to keep from gasping aloud. Luckily, after that first glance, he'd gone back to finish what he was doing, giving her time to catch her breath.

Perhaps she'd been mistaken. He certainly didn't seem to recognise her. But then how could he? The only time they'd ever met her face had been swathed in bandages, and now her hairstyle covered the scars. Even the name wouldn't be familiar to him, since she'd gone back to using her maiden name after Richard's death.

'Sorry to keep you waiting,' he said now, rising from his desk and walking towards her, his hand outstretched. 'I'm Ross Calvert. Miss Waring, isn't it?'

As she took his hand and shook it briefly, Sheila gave him a closer look. Yes, it was the same man. And, of course, she recognised the name. Although she still had to keep in check the instinct to turn and run out of that house as fast as she could go, by now the shock had worn off a little. Clearly he didn't know who she was. All she'd have to do was stay a minute or two, answer a few questions, then decline the job and make her get-away.

'Has my sister filled you in on any of the gory details?' he was asking her now.

'Not really,' she replied. His sister! Of course. The woman who had written the letter to Kate was the child's aunt.

'Well,' Jane Meredith was saying briskly now, 'I'll leave you two to get on with it. Nice to have met you, Sheila. I do hope things will work out here for you.' She laughed. 'I do have a life of my own to get back to.'

When she was gone, Ross Calvert motioned Sheila to the chair in front of his desk, then resumed his seat behind it. He didn't say anything for a moment or two, but just sat there frowning, his long fingers steepled under his chin, as though trying to decide how to begin. Finally he raised his eyes and gave her a long direct look.

'I won't beat about the bush, Miss Waring. I have a serious problem on my hands with my daughter, and I only hope you can help me with it. Poor Jane has been here for weeks, and can't seem to make

any headway. But then, she's a college English pro-
fessor, not a trained therapist.'

'Perhaps you'd better tell me a little about the
child,' Sheila said. 'Then I'd have something to go
on before I decided.'

'Of course.' He got up from his chair and walked
over to the window, staring out over the ocean for
several seconds, his back towards her. Then he
turned around, chin in hand, and crossed over to
stand before her, leaning his narrow hips back
against the desk.

'About a year ago Beth was badly injured in a
serious automobile accident,' he said in a low voice.
'According to the best medical opinion, she should
be walking by now. Instead, she's still confined to
a wheelchair, and although we've tried every
therapy known to man she can't seem to get out of
it.'

'I see,' Sheila replied slowly. 'But if she's already
had such extensive therapy, and nothing has
worked, I don't know what more I could do for
you.'

He ran a hand over his hair and gave her a bleak
look. 'Miss Waring, I'm desperate. You're my last
hope. You come highly recommended and I understand your speciality is working with children. If
you would just give it a try, I'd be eternally
grateful.'

Sheila looked away, biting her lip. Her heart went
out to the man, and, considering that it was her
own husband who'd killed his wife and crippled his
daughter, in a way she owed it to him to help him.
But how could she stay in his house, knowing who

he was? Wouldn't it be a deception? And what if he discovered her real identity?

'Perhaps if I were to meet the girl,' she said at last. 'In my work personalities are important. She may hate me on sight.'

'I hardly think so,' he replied with a smile. 'You seem like a sensible, capable young woman, and you certainly must care something about children, since you've made the care of them your life's work.'

Sheila rose from her chair. 'Well, as I say, suppose you introduce me to her and leave us alone for half an hour or so? Then I'll give you my decision.'

'Fine,' he said, moving towards the door. 'Please, just make yourself at home, and I'll go get her.'

While he was gone, Sheila wandered around the study. It was a pleasant room, very masculine and businesslike, with no frills. A room to work in, panelled in fine-grained wood, with a fireplace in the centre of one wall flanked by bookcases which appeared to be filled with heavy legal tomes.

A large sideboard sat across from it, and set on top was a photograph. Drawn almost against her will, Sheila walked slowly over to inspect it more closely. It was a candid shot of a man, a woman and a small girl, dressed in casual wear, standing in front of a sleek sailboat and smiling into the camera.

The man, of course, was Ross Calvert, obviously a few years younger, with a more carefree boyish look about him than the rather stern man she had met today. The child looked to be around four or

five, with long straight blonde hair caught back by
a wide ribbon.

But it was the woman who took her breath away.
It could only be his dead wife, and she was simply
one of the loveliest creatures Sheila had ever seen.
Her features were delicate and she had the same
long blonde hair as her daughter. It was a fragile
beauty that was only enhanced by the contrast with
the tall dark man standing beside her.

She went over to the window and stared blankly
out at the sea. Ross Calvert's predicament tugged
at her heart, and it was Richard who had created
it. The man obviously loved his daughter deeply
and would do anything for her. If she decided she
could help the girl, didn't she owe it to her—and
her father—to do what she could?

But did she dare stay? The Ross Calvert she'd
met today was a fine figure of a man, a successful
man, obviously, and, except for his deep concern
over his daughter, a man who clearly was born to
command. But she couldn't quite forget the Ross
Calvert she'd encountered on that one awful oc-
casion, over a year ago.

During her long stay in the hospital, recuper-
ating from what seemed like endless surgeries on
her face, she had become acquainted with some of
the other long-term patients on her daily trips to
the sun-room, as well as the regular visitors.

She'd soon noticed that there was one man who
sat apart from all the others. His face was drawn
and haggard and he never joined in the general
conversation. Occasionally one of the others would
speak to him and, while he always answered politely, it was in such terse tones that it hadn't taken

long for them to realise he must be nursing a private grief of his own, and they'd left him alone.

One afternoon the nurse had wheeled her into the sun-room earlier than usual, and for a change it was quite empty. 'I'll just leave you here for a moment, Mrs Fulton,' the nurse said after parking her in her usual spot by the window. She left her then, saying she'd be back shortly with her juice.

Just then, from the other doorway, came the sound of a man's voice. 'So you're Mrs Fulton,' she heard him say.

Thinking it must be one of the doctors, she turned her head to see that same solitary man standing in the doorway. He stared intently at her for one long moment, then began walking slowly towards her, his face like thunder.

'I'm glad to see you up and about, Mrs Fulton,' he said in a voice heavy with sarcasm.

She flinched back from him. 'Who are you?' she asked in a small voice.

He seemed rigid with suppressed fury, and was glaring down at her with murder in his eyes. 'I happen to be the husband of the woman you killed,' he replied in a low, menacing tone.

With that, he turned on his heel and stalked off, passing by the nurse on her way back.

She took one look at Sheila, set the juice on a nearby table and bent over her. 'What is it Mrs Fulton? Is something wrong?'

'Who was that man?' Sheila choked out in a whisper. 'The one who left just as you came in.'

'You mean Mr Calvert? Oh, never mind about him,' the nurse added hastily. 'He's only here visiting——'

'His wife was killed in the accident, wasn't she?' Sheila broke in.

'Mrs Fulton, I really think you'd better speak to Dr Fleming about that.'

She'd asked David about it at the first opportunity, and he'd confirmed her suspicions. What he hadn't mentioned, however, was the fact that the man's daughter had also been seriously injured. Now all the old guilt threatened to erupt again.

Just then she heard the sound of footsteps coming towards the study and turned to see Ross Calvert coming through the door. He was carrying a little girl of seven or eight. She had her arms around her father's neck, clinging to him tightly, and was gazing at Sheila now with a look of terror on her face.

'Darling,' Ross was saying to her in a low, soothing voice, 'this is Miss Waring. I hope she's going to help you walk again.' He glanced at Sheila. 'My daughter. Beth.'

Sheila put on her most reassuring smile and began to walk slowly towards them. 'Hello, Beth,' she said. 'I'm very happy to meet you.'

With each step she took the girl's eyes only became wider with fear, and finally, with a little cry, she buried her face in her father's shoulder. Sheila stopped short and glanced at Ross, whose mouth was set in a grim line, his eyes defeated.

She took another few steps and put a hand lightly on the girl's painfully thin shoulder. 'I'm not going to hurt you, Beth,' she said softly. 'I want to help you.'

But the girl flinched away and began sobbing loudly. Ross gave Sheila a look of such utter misery that once again her heart went out to him. The man was clearly at his wits' end.

By now the girl's sobbing had escalated into screams of terror, and Ross gave Sheila a stricken look. 'I'm sorry,' he said. 'I think I'd better take her back to Jane.'

'Yes, that would be best for now,' Sheila replied.

He hurried out of the door, and while she waited for him to return she mulled over the situation. She'd read Beth's medical history before she came, and from all indications there was no physical reason why she shouldn't be walking now.

In fact, after seeing her with her father, Sheila thought she recognised a familiar pattern in dealing with children's injuries. Whether he knew it or not, Ross Calvert himself was a major contributing factor in his daughter's illness. The question now was whether to tell him so.

When he returned he stood in the doorway looking at her for a few moments, then, with a bleak smile, spread his hands wide and came walking over to her.

'Well, you can see what I'm up against,' he said. 'Do you think you feel up to tackling the situation?'

She returned his smile. 'Believe me, Mr Calvert, I've seen cases just as bad.' She hesitated a moment. 'If I do decide to take the job,' she went on slowly, 'I'd have to insist on a free hand with her. I've found that sometimes loving parents can be the greatest obstacle to their child's recovery.'

He raised his chin and narrowed his eyes, bridling a little, she could tell. 'Let me assure you, Miss Waring, that I love my daughter very much and would do anything to help her get well and live a normal life again.'

'Oh, I have no doubt about that,' she assured him hastily. 'In fact it's because you care so much for her that you can't really help her. It'll take someone more detached, more objective.'

'I see,' he said stiffly. He crossed over to his desk and stood there for a moment staring off into space, a thoughtful expression on his face.

As she watched him, waiting for his response, it suddenly dawned on her that he was a very attractive man, with finely chiselled features and a thick head of coarse dark hair, cut and brushed neatly. He was quite tall and dressed in a pair of well-fitting dark trousers, an open-necked white shirt and grey pullover. She wondered why he'd never married again, but then remembered the look on his face the day he learned his wife had died—the look of a drowning man. A love that powerful wouldn't be forgotten easily.

When he turned back to her, he seemed more relaxed, his expression decisive. 'I assume you know the terms I'm offering?' he said easily. She nodded. 'And are they acceptable?'

'Well, yes,' she replied slowly. 'But I haven't really made up my mind yet whether I want the job.'

He eyed her narrowly. 'You *are* free to take the job, aren't you?' he persisted. 'I mean, you're not married or involved in a relationship you couldn't bear to leave.'

'No,' she replied, bridling a little at the faintly mocking tone. 'To both questions.'

He raised one heavy dark eyebrow. 'Why not?'

Although she was somewhat taken aback at the abrupt query, she recovered her composure quickly and gave him a direct look. 'I don't see what bearing my personal life has on my qualifications,' she replied, her tone pleasant but tinged with frost.

Their eyes locked together for a moment in subtle unspoken conflict. Then he laughed shortly. 'Of course. You're right. I was only curious.' He gave her a lazy look through half-closed eyes. 'You're a very attractive woman, intelligent, capable. I just thought some man would have snapped you up long ago.'

'I can only assure you again that my personal life won't interfere with my work in any way,' she replied in a firm voice.

'I see,' he said gruffly. 'Sorry if I intruded.' He rose from his chair. 'Well, now, shall we get down to business? I really do need you quite badly, Miss Waring, and money is no object. Would a larger salary persuade you?'

'No, the salary is fine.'

'What is it, then?' He gave her a disarming smile. 'If you object to living here, let me assure you that not only do I have a housekeeper who is the soul of respectability, but I'm gone a great deal of the time on business.'

'What is your business, Mr Calvert?' she asked.

'I'm a trial lawyer. My office is in San Francisco and I keep an apartment there to use when I'm in court. In fact, I've turned down more cases than I've taken lately because of Beth. My sister has been wonderful, but she has a life of her own, a job she wants to get back to. With you here, she could do that.'

Still she hesitated. To be fair, shouldn't she tell him who she was? Ross Calvert was obviously a successful man who wielded great power in the world. He was also a man of deep feelings, even though he kept them well-hidden beneath a façade of authority. What would he do if he found out about their mutual past?

He had come around from behind his desk now to stand before her. 'Tell me what I can do to persuade you,' he said in a low voice, leaning down towards her.

She raised her head to look up into his eyes, a deep steely grey, softened now into a silvery hue, and for a moment she had the odd feeling that time was standing still. There was something about the man, the nearness of him, that made her catch her breath. His face was so close to hers now that she could smell the fresh soapy scent of his skin, and see the little lines crinkling at the corners of his eyes under the heavy black brows.

She put a hand to her throat, sensing danger, but impelled by a force she couldn't resist. 'All right, Mr Calvert,' she said at last in a low voice. 'I'll take the job.'

He gave her a warm smile and put a hand on her shoulder. 'Great,' he said. 'Now, how about a drink to celebrate?' He turned and went over to the sideboard. 'What would you like? Sherry? Scotch?'

'Dry sherry, if you have it,' she said in a quavering voice, and got up to join him at the sideboard.

He handed her a glass, then raised his in a toast. 'Well, Miss Waring—Sheila—here's to a happy and fruitful collaboration.'

She took a sip of her wine, then gazed at him over the rim of her glass. 'I hope you're right,' she said with a nervous laugh. 'But as I told you, if I'm to help Beth I must have a free hand with her. No interference from a doting papa. So you may have taken on more than you bargained for.'

'Yes,' he agreed, nodding. 'I can see that. But I have great confidence in you. It's part of my job to judge people accurately, and you're obviously a woman of strong character and firm ideas about right and wrong, qualities I appreciate very much. In fact,' he added with another disarming grin, 'I'm a lot like that myself.'

CHAPTER TWO

A WEEK later Sheila was in her new bedroom in Ross Calvert's house unpacking her belongings.

It was a lovely room, large and airy, with lots of light, and she had her own private bath. Although it was obviously a guest room, with its rather impersonal décor and solid oak furniture, still there were feminine touches in the gathered valance at the windows, a pattern of delicate rosebuds that was repeated in the bedspread, and a frilly lamp on the bedside tables. Touches most likely put there by the dead Laura Calvert.

Through the large bank of windows, she even had a glimpse of the sea, an angry grey on this blustery March day, its swelling surface dotted with white caps. She could even hear the roar of the surf as it crashed against the boulders on the shore far below.

She was also glad to see, off to one side, a kidney-shaped swimming-pool. Not only did she enjoy bathing herself, but it would be excellent therapy for Beth when the weather warmed up.

She had just finished placing the last of her clothing in a dressing-table drawer when there came a light tapping on the door. She glanced quickly into the mirror above the dressing-table to make sure her hair was arranged carefully over the scars high on her forehead, then turned to face the door.

'Come in,' she called.

The door opened, and Jane Meredith stepped inside. 'Are you getting settled all right?' she asked.

'Oh, yes. I didn't bring much.'

'Well, if you'll come with me now, I'll introduce you to Mrs Swenson, Ross's housekeeper. Then I'll be on my way.'

Sheila gave her an alarmed look. 'You're not leaving already! I just got here.'

'Oh, my dear, I've been here far too long as it is,' Jane replied. 'If I don't get back to my husband soon, I may find I don't have one. Not to mention my job.'

'Of course,' Sheila said dubiously. 'But...'

Jane waved a hand in the air. 'You don't need me anyway. In fact,' she went on with a sigh, 'I sometimes think I've probably done Beth more harm than good. Like Ross, I'm too emotionally involved with the girl. I don't have children of my own, you see, so Beth has been very dear to me, especially since her mother's death. Such a tragedy to lose her mother so young.'

'Yes,' Sheila replied stiffly. She looked away as all the old guilt for her part in that tragic death rose up to haunt her. It did no good to tell herself she wasn't responsible. She still *felt* she was, in some way. 'That must have been a terrible thing for both Beth and her father,' she added weakly at last.

Jane gave her a sharp look. 'Well, they'll both just have to get over it, won't they? I mean, life does go on.' Then she smiled and her tone softened. 'And I'm hoping you'll be able to help them do that.'

'I'll try, of course,' Sheila replied. 'But it's a difficult case. When I first met Beth a week ago she was terrified of me. I may not be able to get past that barrier.'

Jane hesitated for a moment. 'I think,' she said in a thoughtful tone, 'that you may find my brother as much a problem as Beth. He's a strong-willed man with depths of emotion he keeps well-hidden on the surface, and he's like a tiger when it comes to his child.'

'Yes, I can see that,' Sheila replied soberly. Then she smiled. 'But I've already taken that into account. I've had a pretty wide experience of problem parents.'

Just then there came another light rapping on the door, and both women looked up to see Ross Calvert standing there, looking from one to the other.

'Am I interrupting something?' he asked lightly.

'Oh, Ross,' Jane said. 'There you are. I was just going to introduce Sheila to Mrs Swenson.'

'I can do that,' he said easily, taking a step inside. 'There's no point in prolonging the farewells. How did Beth take it when you told her you were leaving?'

Jane flushed guiltily. 'Well, I didn't actually mention that I'd be gone for good. I just told her Howard needed me.'

Ross glanced at Sheila. 'You're the expert,' he said. 'What do you think?'

Sheila thought a moment. 'Well,' she began slowly, 'in general I think it's always best to tell children as much of the truth as they can take. At least never lie to them.' She smiled at Jane. 'You really didn't do that, and until she gets used to me it's probably best that she thinks you'll be coming back.'

'Well, that's all right, then,' Jane said with obvious relief. 'I'll just be on my way now. Good luck, Sheila, and if you really need me please call.' She went over to her brother and kissed him on the cheek. 'Goodbye, Ross. Call me soon and. let me know how things are going.'

'Jane,' he said fondly, embracing her, 'I can never thank you enough for all you've done. We couldn't have managed without you.'

'Oh, bosh,' Jane said, reddening. 'I love Beth too, you know.'

'Yes,' he said softly, 'I do know. Now, let me carry your bags out to the car.'

Jane held up a hand. 'That's all taken care of. You stay here and help Sheila get settled.'

With a last little wave, she turned on her heel and strode purposefully out of the door. In a moment there came the sound of a car starting up out in the front drive, then, except for the continuous roar of the surf, silence.

Suddenly shy at being alone in her bedroom with Ross Calvert, Sheila turned to him. He was still standing in the doorway and gazing at her with a rather bemused expression on his lean face. An interesting face, she thought, all definite planes, high cheekbones, a square determined chin, and those deep grey eyes, which held her now in an almost hypnotic attraction.

Finally he smiled and took a step towards her, breaking the spell. 'I'm very glad you decided to take the job,' he said. 'If you need anything, anything at all, just let me know.'

'Thank you, Mr Calvert,' she replied.

'Ross, please,' he said, moving another step towards her. 'I don't like standing on formality in my own home.'

'All right. Ross, then. And as for my needs, the critical issue is to make friends with Beth. If I'm to help her, she's got to trust me.'

'I agree,' he said. 'Just tell me what I can do.'

She laughed nervously. His dominating presence in her bedroom was becoming more unsettling by the minute. He was quite a large man, tall, with broad shoulders and a powerful build, and so filled the room that it seemed much smaller with him in it.

'Well, you may not like it,' she commented lightly.

'Try me.'

'It's just that I'm going to need some time alone with her. As I told you a week ago, sometimes a loving parent can do more harm than good. I must have a free hand, with no interference.'

The smile faded and his expression hardened. 'I see,' he said curtly. 'Well, all I can say is that I'm willing to try anything that might help Beth, and I'll do my best to stay out of your way. As a matter of fact, I should be spending some time in San Francisco right about now anyway. I think I mentioned to you that I have an important trial coming up.'

'Then it seems we understand each other,' she remarked in a tentative voice.

He gave her a crooked smile. 'So far at any rate. Now, shall we go meet my housekeeper?'

'Yes,' she replied. 'But I do want to get started with Beth as soon as possible.'

'Well, she's in the kitchen with Mrs Swenson. Come along and we can kill two birds with one stone.'

As they walked together down the long hallway, Sheila was intensely aware of the tall man beside her. He seemed preoccupied, concerned, she imagined, about her meeting with Beth after what had happened last time.

Sheila was just as glad of the silence. Uppermost in her mind was how to approach Beth. It was essential that the girl learn to trust her. She'd given it a lot of thought over the past week and had finally come up with a plan of attack. She only hoped it would work.

She was so absorbed in her thoughts that she didn't realise he'd made a turning until he bumped into her and she almost lost her footing. He reached out to take her by the arm, steadying her, and the sudden unexpected touch of his hand on her skin was like a jolt of electricity.

She stopped short to recover her balance and looked up at him. Still he held her firmly. The grey eyes glittered down at her for a moment, then abruptly he dropped his hand from her arm, as though he'd just now realised he'd been holding it.

'Sorry,' she said with a little laugh. 'I'm afraid I wasn't paying attention to where I was going.'

'Are you all right?'

'Oh, yes. Just a little clumsy.'

Ever since the accident, her balance had been somewhat shaky from the broken hip. David had told her she'd recover complete mobility and equilibrium in time, but she was still a little unsteady on her feet, especially when she was in unfamiliar surroundings, and still suffered occasional sharp jabs of pain.

'Well, we've arrived at our destination anyway,' he said.

He pushed open a swinging door and she followed him into a large warm kitchen. A tall, stout, grey-haired woman stood at the marble-topped table in the centre of the room rolling out pie crust. Drawn up to the table in her wheelchair was Beth, with her own miniature rolling-pin and a lump of very grimy-looking dough.

'Daddy,' she said excitedly, beaming at him. 'I'm helping Mrs Swenson with...'

Her voice faltered as she caught sight of Sheila, half hidden behind the tall form of her father. A shadow passed over her face and her features scrunched up, an obvious prelude to tears.

Sheila stayed put, watching to see how Ross would handle the situation. He immediately rushed to his daughter's side, got down on his haunches and put a hand under her chin.

'Now, Beth, we talked about this, remember?' The girl nodded dubiously. 'Sheila has come to help you learn how to walk again,' he went on. 'And it's up to you to let her do it.'

Beth darted a quick look at Sheila, then back at her father. 'I'm scared,' she whispered shakily. 'She'll hurt me.'

'No,' he said firmly. 'She will not hurt you. I promise.'

Sheila ground her back teeth together and clenched her fists at her sides, cursing all the doting

parents who lied to their children out of love. Of
course it was going to hurt! Didn't he realise that?
Those disused muscles in the girl's legs would have
to be brought to life again, and a certain amount
of pain was unavoidable.

She glanced at Mrs Swenson. Their eyes met for
a split-second before the older woman looked away,
shaking her head. But in that one brief glance Sheila
was certain she detected the same impatience with
Ross Calvert as she felt herself. There was a possible
ally, she thought. And it looked as though she was
going to need one in this household.

She'd just have to deal with Ross Calvert later.
With luck he'd be leaving soon for his trial. Right
now her primary goal was to win Beth's confidence.

Ignoring Ross, who had risen to his feet by now,
Sheila walked slowly towards the girl in the wheelchair. She was not a tall woman, and, although
she'd always regretted not having a few more inches
in height, her rather short stature was a definite
advantage in dealing with children, since it made
her appear less threatening to them.

She sat down in the chair beside Beth and leaned
back in it, keeping a comfortable distance between
them. 'I've brought you a present, Beth,' she said
in a low, soothing voice.

The girl glanced up at her father, who gave her
a reassuring smile and nodded, then she turned back
to eye Sheila warily. 'What is it?' she asked shyly.

'Oh, you'll have to see it,' Sheila replied with a
laugh. 'I can't describe it.' She rose slowly to her
feet. 'Why don't you let me wheel you to my room
and I'll show it to you?'

Beth wrinkled her forehead, mulling this over. 'All right,' she said at last. Then after a moment's hesitation she added, 'Daddy can come, too.'

But Sheila, quickly seizing her opportunity, had already released the brake and grasped the handles of the chair firmly. 'Oh, we don't need Daddy right now,' she said lightly, pushing the chair before her. 'You can show him later.'

Beth twisted her head around to give her a frightened glance. 'You promise you won't hurt me?'

Sheila shook her head. 'I promise.' At least not today, she added to herself. 'All we'll do now is look at the present.'

She kept moving forward all the while, determined to get the girl alone. At the door she darted one quick glance behind her. Ross was standing where she'd left him, his arms hanging at his sides, his jaw set and grim, staring after her, clearly concerned about the way she'd simply taken charge. But as her eyes flicked to his she could see something like hope in them.

The session with Beth went quite well. The old-fashioned doll Sheila had brought her, with its wardrobe of crinolines and full-skirted petticoats and frilly pantaloons, had made a great hit, as she'd known it would. She'd kept it short, only half an hour, and then wheeled her back to the kitchen, where Mrs Swenson was just putting her pies into the oven.

'I'll leave Beth with you if I may,' she said.

'Oh, sure,' was the reply in a broad Scandinavian accent. 'Beth and me, we can wait for the pies to bake. See, honey?' she said to the girl, showing her a flat plan. 'We bake yours, too.'

'I need to have a word with Mr Calvert,' Sheila said. 'Do you know where he is?'

'Ya, sure,' was the reply. 'In the study.'

'Thanks.'

Sheila started for the door, but before she'd gone far she heard the woman calling to her. 'Miss?' Sheila turned around. 'Yes, Mrs Swenson?'

'I just want to say, well, I'm glad you're here. I can tell you're going to help Beth.'

'That's my plan, Mrs Swenson,' Sheila replied, and the two women exchanged a conspiratorial look.

The study door was closed when she reached it. She hesitated a moment, not wanting to disturb him, but then decided to go ahead and knock. He was paying her an exorbitant salary to treat his daughter, and if she were to earn it she'd need some of his time.

'Yes,' she heard him call. 'Come in.'

She opened the door and stepped inside. He was waiting at his desk, in the position he'd been in the first day she'd met him, poring over a stack of file folders.

'I'm sorry to bother you,' she said, moving to stand before his desk. 'But we need to have a talk about Beth.'

He raised his head and gave her a searching glance, then leaned back in his swivel chair. 'All right. Shoot. And sit down. I don't like people hovering over me.' Then he smiled. 'Especially one with red hair and fire in her bright green eyes. You look like Boadicea, all ready to charge into battle.'

'Oh, I wouldn't say that,' she replied, seating herself. 'But we do have to get one thing clear if I'm to do anything for Beth.'

'Such as?'

She gave him a direct look. There was no point in beating about the bush. 'Well, for one thing, as I mentioned to Jane earlier, you should never lie to her.'

His eyes flew open, then narrowed at her. 'Lie to her? I wouldn't dream of lying to her! What makes you say a thing like that?'

'You told her I wouldn't hurt her,' she said. 'And at some point I'm going to have to do just that.'

'No,' he said, frowning. 'I can't allow that.' His voice was flat and with a definite note of finality in it.

She placed her elbows on top of the desk and leaned towards him, gazing at him intently. 'Tell me, Ross,' she said in a dead serious tone. 'Do you want your daughter to walk again or don't you?'

'Of course I do. How can you even ask such a question? Why else do you think I've brought you down here, into my home—at great expense, I might add—if that wasn't uppermost in my mind?'

His anger seemed to be escalating by the moment, and somehow she'd have to come up with a way to defuse it. Without removing her eyes from that hard, steely gaze, she sighed deeply and settled back in her chair, searching her mind for a way to get through to him.

'Let me be quite clear about this,' she said. 'You may wield a certain degree of power and control in the world of business, the law, but you're obviously helpless when it comes to Beth. Now, where her condition is concerned, I happen to be the expert. That's why you hired me. And I'm telling you right now, as plainly as I can, that she'll never walk again without having to suffer some pain. I'll keep it as light as I possibly can,' she added hastily. 'I won't push her or give her more than I think she can handle. And I will never, ever lie to her.' She spread her hands. 'Now, if you can't live with that, then I'd better pack my bags and leave. There'd be no point in even getting started.'

As she watched the play of emotion on his features that he couldn't quite hide, she could almost feel sorry for him. He was a man accustomed to control, of himself and his world, and was clearly having a lot of trouble accepting the fact that in this case he truly was helpless. He *had* to rely on her judgement, and he didn't like it one bit.

Suddenly he got up out of his chair and went over to the window. It was a grey morning, the fog drifting in over the ocean, and the landscape seemed bleak and forbidding, the pleasant room stark and shadowy. He stood there for a moment, rubbing his hand over the back of his neck. Then he turned around to face her.

'All right. You've made your point. What do you suggest?'

'You said you had a trial coming up and should be spending more time in your San Francisco office, isn't that right?'

'Yes,' was the terse reply.

'Then why don't you just go?' She got up and went over to him, gazing up at him earnestly. 'If you don't trust me, then you should fire me now. But if you do, then you've got to let me do this my way.' She laughed uneasily, to break the tension. 'And you can ask Mrs Swenson to keep an eye on me if you like. She's obviously fond of Beth and won't let me harm her.'

He shook his head. 'That won't be necessary,' he said in a stiff voice. 'All right. I might as well leave right away, then.'

By afternoon the fog had cleared and a pale March sun was struggling to break through the lingering mist. Ross had taken Beth into Monterey for a farewell luncheon, and Mrs Swenson was in her own room watching the afternoon soap operas.

After a solitary lunch in the kitchen, Sheila decided to take a walk around the extensive grounds. She particularly wanted to examine the swimming-pool. As soon as the weather warmed up, she planned to take advantage of it in her treatment of Beth. Swimming was wonderful therapy for atrophied muscles, and most children enjoyed the water. Best of all it was completely painless.

Although the pool seemed to be disused and uncared for, with leaves floating on the surface, the water looked clean and the pump was running. She knelt down and put a hand in the water to test the temperature. It turned out to be quite warm, which meant it had to be heated, and they wouldn't have to wait for warm weather after all.

She had just risen to her feet when she heard footsteps coming towards her. She raised her hand to shield her eyes from the sun, and for a moment her heart stood still. Walking towards her was the woman in the photograph in the study—Ross Calvert's dead wife! But that couldn't be! She simply stood there for a moment, rooted to the spot, staring blankly at the apparition, which kept coming steadily towards her, a tall, slim woman with long blonde hair.

'Hello,' the woman called when she was just a few feet away. 'You must be the new therapist.'

As she came closer, Sheila could see that she'd been mistaken. Still, the likeness was astounding. The same hair, the same bone-structure in the narrow, aristocratic-looking features, the same slim build. It had only been a trick of the light that fooled her.

'Yes,' she replied. 'I'm Sheila Waring.'

The blonde smiled and held out a hand. 'And I'm Eleanor Caldwell, Ross's next-door neighbour. How do you do?' After they'd shaken hands, Eleanor looked around. 'I notice Ross's car is gone. Do you know when he'll be back?'

'He just took Beth into town for lunch, but they should be back shortly.'

She hesitated, wondering if she should invite Eleanor inside to wait for him, offer her tea or a drink. She had no idea how hospitable she was expected to be to this neighbour of Ross's. For all she knew he might want to avoid her.

'Well, that'll give us a chance to get acquainted, won't it?' Eleanor replied pleasantly. She sat down in one of the deck-chairs by the side of the pool. 'You can't see my house from here because of the trees, but I just live up the road.' She glanced up at Sheila, who was still standing uncertainly before her. 'Won't you sit down?' she asked with a wave of her hand towards the other chair.

A little taken aback at the woman's proprietorial air, Sheila didn't know quite what to do. It would be rude to continue standing after the invitation to join her, but on the other hand it could be a mistake to encourage her.

Luckily, she was saved having to make the decision by the sound of Ross's car roaring up the drive. It was a racy sports model she couldn't identify, but it looked foreign and the top was down, a rather incongruous vehicle for a man who appeared as conservative in his tastes as Ross Calvert.

'Oh,' Eleanor laughed, rising to her feet. 'I see he took Laura's Ferrari. He always hated that car, but Beth loves it—and as you've probably gathered by now,' she added, giving Sheila a knowing look, 'he'll do anything for Beth.'

The car had pulled up in front of the house by now. Ross had got out and was unfolding Beth's chair. If he realised Eleanor was there he made no sign, and Sheila began to think she'd done right by not encouraging her. Just then he raised his head to look directly at them. They were still standing beside the pool, but even at that distance, some fifty feet, Sheila could see the slow smile that spread across his face.

Eleanor raised a hand and started walking quickly towards him. 'Hello, Ross,' she called on her way. 'Just thought I'd stop by to get acquainted with Beth's new therapist and offer my help if she needs it.'

Sheila, following slowly behind her, rolled her eyes at that last comment. It was the first she'd heard of any offer of help! By the time she arrived at the car, Eleanor was opening Beth's door and leaning over to pick her up.

'There now,' she cooed. 'Just let your aunty Eleanor help you out. Ross,' she called, 'if you'll just bring the chair around I can manage with Beth.'

Sheila stood off to one side watching as Ross wheeled the chair over and the two of them got Beth settled down. It was almost as though they made up a family unit. Except for the wheelchair, the little tableau could even have been a pose for the photograph in the study and, considering Eleanor's remarkable resemblance to Laura Calvert, with the same people in it.

Just then Mrs Swenson appeared at the top of the brick steps leading up to the front door. 'I finished packing for you, Mr Calvert,' she said in a loud voice as she descended the steps. She took a firm grip on Beth's chair. 'I take her inside now. Time for her nap.' She turned to Sheila. 'Will you help me get the chair up the steps, miss?'

Grateful for the invitation, Sheila nodded and went ahead of her to grasp the handlebars while they both lifted the chair. Since the girl was as light as a feather, it wasn't hard, and Mrs Swenson could easily have managed by herself.

When they reached the porch, Beth gazed up at Sheila with something like panic in her eyes, then turned her head back towards her father. 'Daddy?' she called. 'You won't leave without saying goodbye?'

'No, of course not,' he called back to her. 'Remember, we talked about it at lunch. You're to be a good girl for Sheila and Mrs Swenson, and I'll be back as soon as I can.'

Not wanting to press her luck, once inside the house Sheila let Mrs Swenson take charge of the girl, and started off down the hall towards the kitchen, thinking to make herself a cup of tea. As she passed by the open study door, however, she noticed that it gave her a direct view through the window of the front driveway. She hesitated a moment, but the temptation was too strong to resist.

Creeping over to the window, and feeling like a criminal, she positioned herself behind the curtains so that she could look out at Eleanor and Ross without being seen. At first glance, they seemed to be arguing, and although their voices were not clearly audible she could get the general drift of the conversation from the few words she could hear.

Apparently Eleanor had not been told that Ross planned to leave for San Francisco that very day, and was quite annoyed at the fact. From the way she stood there, hands on her hips, glaring up at him, she had clearly expected to be consulted. For his part, Ross just stood there before her, solid as a rock, his arms crossed in front of him, his face expressionless, waiting for her to finish.

When she finally shut up and he started speaking, it was in such a low voice that Sheila couldn't make out any of it. Whatever it was, though, it seemed to mollify Eleanor completely, and by the time he finished she was smiling brilliantly at him. Then, leaning a little closer, she raised her arms up around his neck, pressed herself against him, and lifted her face to his.

He seemed to hesitate a fraction of a second, then slowly his arms came around her waist. They kissed then, briefly, although it seemed to Sheila that Ross was allowing himself to be kissed rather than taking the initiative. Still, she thought wryly, neither was he throwing up his hands in horror at the prospect of tearing himself out of her arms. As she watched, in fact, the embrace seemed to heat up visibly, and it was definitely not the way merely friendly neighbours kissed.

So, she thought, unable to tear her eyes away, that's the way the wind blows. It didn't look as though Ross Calvert had lived a strictly celibate life since his wife died after all. Interesting. And strangely irritating. But that reaction made no sense. In fact, it felt uncomfortably like jealousy!

What did she care what the man did or whom he did it with? His love life was no concern of hers. All she wanted was to get him out of here so that she could start working in earnest with Beth. It would be hard enough considering the months of inactivity behind her, but impossible with her father hovering over her, monitoring every step.

Just at that moment, he raised his head and glanced past the still clinging Eleanor directly towards the house. Afraid he might notice her there staring out at him, Sheila quickly turned away, hoping he hadn't seen her, and scooted out of the room.

As she made her way towards the kitchen to make herself that cup of tea, she decided to invite Mrs Swenson to join her. She was very curious about the status of Ross's relationship with Eleanor, and Mrs Swenson would undoubtedly know exactly how matters stood between them.

Of course, she assured herself hastily as she set the water on to boil, her interest was only professional. She needed to know as much as possible about the Calvert family life in order to do her job well.

She had just poured out two cups of tea and was going to look for Mrs Swenson when she heard the front door open and close, then footsteps coming towards the kitchen. She turned to see Ross standing in the doorway. Their eyes met and held for one brief moment, then Sheila reached for the extra cup she'd poured and held it out.

'Would you like a cup of tea before you go?' she asked.

'No,' he said absently, coming inside. 'No, thank you. I think it's best that I leave right away. Beth and I had a long talk at lunch about it, and she understands that I really do have to go. I don't think she'll give you any trouble on that score.'

'Oh, good,' she said. 'I'm glad. And I agree. It's not going to be easy for her, and the sooner you leave the better.'

Still he lingered, and Sheila had to wonder why. He seemed to have something on his mind, something he was having trouble saying.

'Ross,' she said, 'if you're worried about my mistreating Beth, let me assure you again——'

'No,' he broke in curtly. 'If I didn't trust you I wouldn't leave.' He gave her a wry smile. 'I really don't have much choice. I *have* to trust you.' He cocked his head to one side, and the smile broadened, softening his features. 'I'm convinced by now that you really do know your business professionally and that you're a woman of sterling character. But, what's even more important to me, you care about Beth, her future.'

'Of course I do!' she exclaimed. 'My work is my life!'

He pursed his lips, frowning. 'That's not much of a life for an attractive young woman, is it? Although,' he added with a dry laugh, 'I guess the same could be said about me.' Then he sobered. 'Which brings me to something I feel I should make clear to you.' He paused for a moment. 'It's about Eleanor. It's not what you think.'

'I don't think anything,' she assured him hastily, which was a patent lie, but which she felt she had to say. 'It's none of my affair.'

'But I think it is. Whatever affects me—at least at this point—affects Beth, affects her recovery. That's everything to me. More important than my work, and certainly more important than Eleanor Caldwell. She and my wife were close friends, and when Laura died she took it upon herself to pinch-hit for her. With Beth, mainly, but...' And here his voice trailed off. 'In any case, I don't want you to think I've been carrying on some lurid affair under my daughter's nose, that's all,' he added stiffly. 'Now, I'll just go say one last goodbye to Beth and be on my way. If you need anything— anything at all—you're to call me. Mrs Swenson has my number both at the office and the apartment.'

With that, he turned on his heel and left Sheila standing there, still holding the now cold cup of tea and wondering why she felt so elated at the news that he and the delectable Eleanor Caldwell were not romantically involved.

CHAPTER THREE

THREE weeks later, on a warm sunny morning in April, just as Sheila was finishing her morning coffee, Jane Meredith arrived unexpectedly.

'How nice to see you, Jane,' she said warmly when she opened the door to her. 'Please come in. How about a cup of coffee?'

'I'd love one,' Jane replied, stepping inside.

'What brings you here?' Sheila asked as they went together towards the kitchen. 'Anything special?'

'Well, to tell you the truth, I've been feeling a little guilty about dashing off the way I did practically the moment you arrived. It wouldn't have hurt me to stay another day or two to help you get settled.'

Sheila laughed. 'Oh, you can set your mind at rest about that. Believe me, it was the best thing you could have done for all concerned.'

They had almost reached the kitchen by now, and could hear Mrs Swenson inside bustling about, and the chatter of Beth's childish voice. Jane stopped short just outside the door and put a hand on Sheila's arm.

'How is it going?' she asked in a low voice. 'Any progress at all with Beth?'

'Yes,' Sheila replied with a bright smile. 'I'm happy to say there is. But it's slow going. I have a year of inactivity to overcome, and it's not going to happen overnight. But yes, we have made definite progress.'

It was true. Once she'd gained Beth's trust and made her understand that there would necessarily be some pain involved in her therapy, she'd made remarkable progress. By now she was at least able to stand unaided. The important thing was that the girl really did want to walk again.

Jane gave her arm a squeeze. 'I'm delighted to hear it.' She laughed. 'And I have no doubt that a major reason for your success so far was that you shooed Ross out of here that same day.'

Sheila smiled at her. 'Well, let's just say that once he grasped the fact that he was only hampering my efforts by his concern he saw the wisdom of leaving me alone with her.'

'Well, that's quite a feat in itself,' Jane said, rolling her eyes. 'With his ego, getting my brother to admit he can't move the sun and stars by his own will must have taken some doing.'

'Not really. It's actually quite simple. His love for Beth is far more powerful than his ego.' She grinned. 'Even granting that he owns a pretty king-sized one.'

Jane nodded. 'Yes. I agree. He dotes on the girl. Listen, Sheila, before we go inside, I wanted to ask you if it would be all right to take Beth down to Carmel with me today. Do a little shopping, have lunch.'

'Of course. She'd love it, I'm sure. And I have a favour to ask you.'

'Name it.'

'Now that the weather is warming, I'd like to use the pool for Beth's therapy. I'd noticed that the pump was running and that the water is heated, but it does need cleaning. Do you suppose Ross would mind if I contacted someone to service it on a regular basis?'

'I'm sure he wouldn't,' was the prompt reply. 'But if you're worried about it, why not call him and ask him?'

Actually, in the past three weeks, Sheila had considered calling him several times, but always hesitated. She knew that he called often to talk to Beth, but since Mrs Swenson always answered the telephone and he never asked to speak to her she hadn't wanted to bother him. But it really was important to get Beth in the water, and she should have his permission to service the pool first.

'Yes,' she said at last. 'I guess that's what I should do.'

That evening, after Beth was safely tucked in bed, Sheila went into the study to call Ross. Mrs Swenson had given her both telephone numbers, but since it was past eight o'clock he was more likely to be at the apartment than his office.

She stood beside the desk for some moments gazing down at the telephone and wondering why in the world her heart was fluttering around so erratically and her stomach felt so hollow. Surely not at the prospect of speaking to Ross Calvert. He was only her employer, after all.

Then her eyes strayed to the photograph on the sideboard, and the sudden thought came to her that she'd give a great deal to see that look on his face again, smiling, carefree, his eyes alight with the sheer joy of living.

Dismissing her idle thoughts hurriedly, not to mention the direction they were leading her in, she snatched up the telephone and dialled before she could change her mind. It rang several times before she finally heard the click of the receiver at the other end.

'Hello,' came a woman's voice, a voice whose dulcet tones Sheila recognised immediately as belonging to Eleanor Caldwell.

'Hello,' she replied. 'I'm trying to reach Ross Calvert.'

'Who's calling, please?' came the abrupt response.

'This is Sheila Waring, his daughter's——'

'Oh, yes. The therapist. Just a minute.'

There was a muffled sound as though she'd put her hand over the mouthpiece, and Sheila could hear her calling to Ross. In just a few seconds he came on the line.

'Sheila?' he said in a voice tight with concern. 'What's wrong?'

'Nothing's wrong, Ross,' she reassured him quickly. 'Nothing at all. In fact, everything's going quite well.'

She heard him expel a deep sigh. 'Good lord, woman,' he said in an irritated tone. 'You frightened me out of my wits!'

'I'm sorry if I alarmed you,' she replied stiffly, 'but I need to ask you something.'

'Well, what is it?' he enquired brusquely.

Growing rather irritated herself by now, Sheila was half tempted to slam the receiver down in his ear. He had some nerve, after all, blaming her for upsetting him when he was up there in San

Francisco playing around with his blonde neighbour. Especially after he'd assured her that there was nothing like that going on between them.

Instead she put on her haughtiest voice. 'Since it's obvious you have other things on your mind, I'll be brief. I'd like to use the swimming-pool as part of Beth's therapy, and just wanted your permission to hire a company to get it in shape and service it.'

'Oh, of course. Do whatever you like. Just charge it to me.'

'Thank you. I'll say goodbye, then and let you get back to—whatever it was I interrupted.'

'Now look here,' he said in a low voice. 'I already explained about that.'

'And I already told you there was no need to explain anything to me. I'm only your employee, after all, not your keeper.'

He gave a harsh laugh. 'Well, you're sure as hell putting on a good imitation of one!'

'I'm sorry,' she intoned loftily. 'I just don't like being lied to.' She could have bitten her tongue out the moment the words escaped her lips, but it was too late to take them back now.

'Listen, I can't talk to you now. I can only repeat what I told you before. It's not what you think.' He paused for a moment. 'As you probably know I talk to Beth just about every night. Is she really doing as well as she thinks she is?'

'Yes, she is,' she replied, thawing a little. 'We're making fine progress. Your sister stopped by today to take her on a little jaunt to Carmel, and she seems to have had a wonderful time.'

'That's great,' he said. 'In fact, I've been thinking. It looks as though my case might be settled out of court soon and we won't go to trial after all. How would you feel about my coming down for a visit? I don't mean to interfere,' he added hastily. 'I'd just like to see Beth.'

Sheila mulled this over for a moment. He seemed sincere enough about not interfering, and she could well understand his desire to see for himself how his daughter was coming along.

'Of course,' she said at last. 'It's your home, after all.'

He laughed. 'You wouldn't think so the way you rushed me out of there. Anyway, I don't know when I can get away, so better not say anything to Beth just yet.'

They said goodbye then, and after she'd hung up Sheila stood there for a long moment her hand still on the receiver, until she realised she was grinning rather foolishly from ear to ear.

The very next day Sheila got the name of the service company Ross had dealt with in the past from Mrs Swenson. She contacted them, and by the end of the week the pool was sparkling clean and ready for use.

Luckily the warm weather held as well, so that the only problem was going to be getting Beth into it. The girl seemed to trust her by now, but she wasn't sure how far that trust went. Her legs were so disused that she would be helpless in the water, and would have to rely on Sheila for her very life.

Although she knew the best way to handle it was to take a firm stand right from the beginning, it was also true that a more oblique approach would probably carry her further at this point.

She was still debating the issue one morning at breakfast. She and Beth and Mrs Swenson were seated at the round table by the window, the bright spring sunshine streaming in, eating bacon and eggs and glancing through the morning paper, when all of a sudden Mrs Swenson let out a sharp yelp and held up her section.

'Well, my stars!' she exclaimed. 'Beth, see what I found!'

She turned the page around and held it up so that Beth and Sheila could both see what it was that had so caught her attention.

'Oh, look!' Beth cried excitedly. 'It's a picture of Daddy.'

Sheila quickly scanned the bold-face headline: PROMINENT ATTORNEY WINS HUGE SETTLEMENT IN PATENT INFRINGEMENT CASE. Below it was a grainy photograph of Ross, just coming down the steps of a building, dressed in a conservative business suit, carrying a briefcase, and inches taller than any of the reporters who surrounded him.

Her first thought was that that meant he'd be coming home soon. She took the paper from Mrs Swenson and began to read aloud:

'Ross Calvert, a senior partner in Calvert and Matheson, one of the city's most prestigious law firms, has just announced the settlement of the patent infringement lawsuit he recently brought in Superior Court. Although Mr Calvert declined to specify the numbers involved, on the basis that there were still many details to iron out

in the next several days, rumour has it that his
opponent agreed on a figure well into the
millions.'

When she'd finished reading, she turned to Beth.
'Well, Beth, you can be very proud of your father.
And it looks as though he'll be coming home to see
you before long.'

'How long?' the girl asked eagerly.

'Oh, probably not for a few weeks. But I'm sure
he'll call you and let you know.'

The girl looked so pleased and seemed so relaxed
and happy at the prospect of seeing her father again
that Sheila decided now was as good a time as any
to broach her swimming project.

'You know, Mrs Swenson,' she said, turning to
the housekeeper, 'it's such a beautiful day I think
I'll go for a swim this morning now that the pool
is all ready to use.'

'Good idea,' Mrs Swenson replied, nodding
firmly.

'Would you care to join me?' Sheila asked
playfully.

Mrs Swenson snorted loudly. 'Hah!' was all she
said, and got up to pour herself another cup of
coffee.

Sheila turned to Beth. 'How about you, Beth?'
she asked lightly. 'Some light exercise in the water
will be very good therapy for your legs.'

'Oh, no. No, thank you,' the girl said. 'I can't
swim.'

Sheila threw up her hands in mock-horror. 'Can't
swim!' Then she smiled and put a hand on the girl's
shoulder. 'Well, I'll just have to teach you, then,

won't I? Wouldn't that be a nice surprise for Daddy when he returns?'

She immediately recognised the look of panic in the girl's eyes, which were a deep clear grey, just like her father's. She gave the shoulder a squeeze, then dropped her hand.

'Well, at least you can get on your bathing suit and dabble your feet in the water while you watch me. Then we'll see later about the swimming. OK?'

The girl nodded dubiously. Still, she'd gone that far without being forced, and even that small concession was a step in the right direction, Sheila thought.

From then on they had regular morning sessions in the pool. All Sheila had brought with her in the way of swimwear was an old blue knit tank suit left over from her college days, and, while it wasn't exactly flattering, neither was she planning on entering a bathing beauty contest, after all.

She was a little worried at first, however, that the bathing suit did reveal the scars on her upper thigh from her hip surgery and that the smaller scars high on her forehead were also visible when her heavy auburn hair was wet. In fact, Beth asked her about them the very first day.

Determined not to lie, Sheila answered truthfully, that she'd been in an accident. To her surprise, Beth seemed delighted, as though it gave them a bond in common, and her own complete recovery even seemed to encourage the girl.

As it turned out, it only took two days to lure the girl into the pool. At first she remained sitting on the top step dabbling her feet in the water, then gradually she scooted down each step in turn until she was allowing Beth to hold her while she floated. By the end of a week she was kicking her legs, feebly at first, then with more vigour, and Sheila decided the time had come to let her strike out on her own.

'I'm going to let go now, Beth,' she said in a low, soothing voice. 'I want to see how far you can swim by yourself.'

The girl turned around, panic in her eyes. 'Sheila . . .'

'Don't worry,' Sheila said firmly. 'I won't let you sink. You trust me, don't you?'

The girl nodded, and Sheila loosened her hold. For a moment it was touch and go, with a lot of splashing and thrashing around, but in the end she did it. Sheila followed her along every inch of the way, giving encouragement, when all of a sudden Beth looked up and began to squeal happily.

'Daddy, Daddy!' she cried. 'Look at me! I'm swimming!'

A cold chill gripped Sheila's heart. It couldn't be, she thought in a panic as she slowly turned her head. But it was. He was standing there in his shirt-sleeves, his suit jacket slung over one shoulder, his tie loosened, and gazing at his daughter with a be-atific expression on his face, as though all his prayers had been answered.

He got down on his haunches at the side of the pool and held out his arms. Beth paddled towards him, until she was close enough for him to reach out for her. As he picked her up and gathered her into his arms, he glanced over her head, his eyes seeking Sheila's, and the look of gratitude and joy he gave her made all the past weeks of effort worth every minute.

'Well, darling,' he said to his daughter. 'Look what you've done to me. I'm soaking wet and I'll have to change.'

'Come and swim with us, Daddy!' the girl begged.

Sheila's heart sank. 'Oh, not today, Beth,' she said quickly. 'It's almost time for lunch.' She glanced up to see the housekeeper coming towards the pool. 'In fact, here comes Mrs Swenson now. You can have a swim with your father after your nap this afternoon.'

'Welcome home, Mr Calvert,' Mrs Swenson said, putting her arms out to take Beth from him. 'This young lady needs to get dried off and fed. Lunch in half an hour.'

The minute Sheila had first caught sight of Ross, she'd ducked her body beneath the surface of the water, suddenly very conscious of the way the thin knit material of her suit clung to her when it was wet. Now, while he chatted with Mrs Swenson, she seized the opportunity to move off to the deep end.

The housekeeper was carrying Beth into the house now, but to her dismay Ross remained right where he was, still standing there and staring directly at her with an intent, narrow-eyed gaze. With only Beth as an audience the revealing wet suit hadn't mattered, but now she quailed under that silent scrutiny. She couldn't stay there forever. She'd have to get out eventually. Her towel was on the chair where she'd left it. Once out of the pool she could make a beeline for it and hope he wouldn't notice anything.

Taking a deep breath, she heaved herself up over the edge, got quickly up on her feet, and started towards the chair. But she hadn't taken into account her erratic hip, and before she'd gone halfway it buckled under her. She would have fallen flat on her face if he hadn't rushed to her side and caught hold of her from behind, and just in time.

As luck would have it, his right hand settled firmly on her breast, and at the sudden unexpected touch she felt as though a jolt of electricity had shot through her. Although he must have realised it himself by now, his hand lingered for a fraction longer than was necessary.

When he finally let her go, she grabbed her towel off the chair and draped it around her shoulders. Then she turned around slowly, a bright smile on her lips, dismissing the little incident—actually hardly an 'incident' at all—but when she saw the look on his face her smile faltered. He was frowning slightly, but in puzzlement rather than anger, as though he'd been taken somewhat off guard himself.

'Thanks for the helping hand,' she said lightly. 'I'm not the most graceful creature in the world, especially on these slick wet tiles.' Still he continued to stare wordlessly at her. 'Well,' she said, turning from him, 'I'd better go get dressed. It's almost time for lunch.'

But before she'd taken the first step she felt his hand on her arm, and another lightning jolt went through her.

'Don't go,' he said in a low voice. 'We need to talk.' She turned around to face him, a question in her eyes. 'About Beth,' he added, dropping his hand. 'I'm truly amazed at the progress you've made with her.' He gave a dry laugh. 'Most likely due largely to my absence, I take it.'

She smiled. 'Well, I wouldn't put it quite as bluntly as that, but I'll have to admit it did help to have her all to myself these past several weeks.'

They started walking together towards the house. 'Well, whatever the reason,' he said, 'I'm deeply grateful. What do you think by now? Will she ever walk again?'

Although he tried to hide it under a stiff reserve, she was well aware of the pain in his voice, and her heart went out to him. 'Of course she will,' she pronounced stoutly. 'There never was any medical reason why she shouldn't. She just needed a little push.' She hesitated a moment. 'As a matter of fact, all I've really done so far is get her leg muscles in better condition through massage and mild iso- metrics. And of course the swimming helps.'

They had reached the house by now, and she stopped at the door to give him a hard, direct look. 'Actually,' she went on, 'I haven't even begun the really difficult part of her therapy.'

His jaw tightened. 'What do you mean?'

'Only that I've spent most of our time together gaining her trust. At some point, however, she's going to have to wake up those muscles, and it's not going to be without some pain.'

'I see,' he replied. 'Of course, you must do what's best for her. You're the expert.'

'Good. I'm glad you agree. Now, I must shower and dress for lunch or Mrs Swenson will be offended.'

'But we still need to have that talk,' he said in a firm voice. 'Alone. And I don't mean about Beth.'

As she showered and dressed, then later, sitting around the luncheon table listening to Beth chatter to her father, Sheila mulled over that last statement. What reason could he have for wanting to talk to her alone if it wasn't about Beth? She noticed, too, that, although he seemed to be giving Beth all his attention, from time to time he would glance in her direction, with the same rather baffled look he'd given her by the pool.

Then, just as she was in the middle of a long gulp of iced tea, it hit her. He'd seen the scars on her face and thigh! That must be the reason for the strange looks, too. Her heart began to pound and she almost choked on her tea.

It didn't take her long, however, to come to her senses and see that she was making a mountain out of a molehill. Even if he did ask her about the scars, even if she admitted the truth, that she'd been in an automobile accident, there was no possible way he could connect her to the collision that killed his wife and crippled Beth. That one time he'd spoken to her in the hospital, her face had been heavily bandaged. Even her name was different now. She was no longer Mrs Fulton, but Miss Waring.

Immediately after lunch, Beth went to take her nap and Mrs Swenson retired to her soaps, and they were left alone. Ross got up from his chair and stretched widely. He'd changed from his business suit to a pair of dark chinos and a loose-knit white shirt, its short sleeves revealing strongly muscled

upper arms and sinewy forearms lightly sprinkled
with silky black hairs.

'How about a walk, Sheila?' he said with a smile.
'There's a great view from the bluff.'

'All right,' she agreed, rising to her feet. 'I'd like
that.'

They went outside and strolled along in silence
past the swimming-pool and around the heavy bank
of shrubbery until they came to the rocky bluff. It
was a magnificent view, the sea almost flat today
and an intense blue, the sun directly overhead
casting its bright reflection on the smooth surface,
the incoming tide crashing against the giant
boulders down below.

Further out there were a few boats drifting lazily
around, their sails reefed in the calm weather. There
was only a slight breeze here at the edge of the cliff,
and except for the constant cawing of the seagulls
as they wheeled and dipped over the shore scav-
enging for food it was very still.

Sheila was intensely aware of the tall man
standing next to her. She gave him a quick sideways
glance. He was squinting a little in the bright sunshine, and his dark hair was slightly ruffled in the
gentle breeze. He was just a few feet away from
her, his hands in the pockets of his trousers.

Finally he turned to her. 'I want to thank you
again for the way you've helped Beth. It seems you
were right when you said I was only hampering her
progress by hovering over her.' He laughed shortly.
'I didn't even realise that's what I was doing.'

'Well, it's a common problem. Believe me, you
aren't the first loving parent I've had to do battle
with. Your first concern is to protect your child

from harm, while mine is to make her well. They sound like the same thing, but they're actually quite different. And,' she added with a smile, 'often at cross-purposes.'

'What you're saying is that since you're not emotionally involved you're better equipped to do that—make her well.'

'Don't mistake me. It's not that I don't have feelings. I've grown very fond of Beth. But I am trained in this work, and most parents aren't.'

'I know. Believe me, I checked into your background quite thoroughly before I even agreed to interview you.'

She gave him a sharp look, wondering just how much Kate had told him about her past. 'That was a wise precaution,' she said in a tight voice.

'Oh, you came very highly recommended.' He gave her a quizzical look. 'But I learned absolutely nothing about your personal life.'

She breathed an inward sigh of relief and gave him a quick smile. 'Does that matter?' she asked lightly.

He shrugged. 'Not really, I guess. But I am curious. You may even have a husband, for all I know.'

'No,' she said slowly. 'I don't have a husband. But I have been married,' she added. 'He died.'

A shadow passed across his face. 'I'm sorry,' he said. 'I know what that's like. But surely you have some personal life?' he persisted. 'An important relationship. Some kind of commitment.' The grey eyes swept over her. 'You're a very attractive woman.'

She thought of David, but that wasn't a commitment. She liked him a lot and was grateful for all he'd done for her after the accident, but she knew there was no future for them and she had never encouraged him to think there might be.

She looked away from him. 'No,' she said. 'There's no one.'

He moved a step closer to her. 'I can hardly believe that,' he said in a low voice.

It was a tense moment. Sheila felt off-balance, unsure of what he was driving at. Was he coming on to her? No, that wasn't possible. He was just grateful, that was all. Still, he did say he found her attractive.

She raised her eyes to meet his, but just then there came the sound of a car roaring up the drive, just barely visible through the mass of shrubbery. When she turned towards it, she recognised the dark blue Mercedes immediately.

David! What in the world was he doing here? She glanced back at Ross, to see that he was scowling darkly.

'Now, who the hell could that be?' he said.

'I—I think it might be for me,' she replied.

He gave her a questioning look, then nodded abruptly. 'Well, then, we'd better go find out, hadn't we?'

They started back to the house and arrived just in time to see David getting out of the car. When he caught sight of Sheila his eyes lit up and he came walking towards her.

'Sheila!' he called, holding out his arms.

She moved into his embrace, and he kissed her lightly on the cheek. 'Well, David,' she said. 'What brings you here?'

'I had a consultation in Monterey that finished up early, and since I was in the neighbourhood I thought I'd look in on you.' He held her at arms' length, looking down into her eyes. 'It's been a long time, Sheila,' he said softly. 'I've missed you.'

All the while, she was uncomfortably aware of Ross, still standing off to one side, just within the range of her peripheral vision. She turned to him now.

'Ross, I'd like to introduce David Fleming. *Dr* Fleming, actually. David, this is Ross Calvert, my patient's father.'

While the two men shook hands, Sheila watched them anxiously. Of course she was glad to see David, but he couldn't have shown up at a more inopportune time, just as she'd been assuring Ross that there was no man in her life, and when he had seemed to be putting their relationship on a more personal level.

'David was one of my supervisors during my early training,' she said now.

'Oh, a little more than that, I hope,' he said with a smile. 'In fact, it's such a lovely day, I thought we could drive down to Carmel, perhaps have dinner.' He turned to Ross. 'How about it, Calvert? Can you spare her for the rest of the day?'

'Of course,' Ross said easily. He darted a rather mocking glance at Sheila. 'She's all yours. Now, if you'll excuse me, I have some things to attend to in the house. Nice to have met you, Dr Fleming.'

With a curt nod, he turned on his heel and began striding towards the house. As she watched him go, Sheila had the almost irresistible compulsion to run after him, to explain that it wasn't what he thought it was, that David was only a friend. In fact, she was really rather irritated at David for showing up out of the blue like that with no warning, and then just assuming she'd go with him. Asking *Ross's* permission, for heaven's sake.

She turned on him now. 'You know, David, I think you could have asked me if I wanted to go before checking with Ross,' she said in an accusing voice.

'I'm sorry, Sheila,' he said. 'It's just that I don't have the chance to get away often. And I've missed you.'

When she saw the hurt look in his pale blue eyes, she regretted her words immediately. 'I know, David,' she said with a sigh. 'I'm sorry, too. And I'd like to go for that drive, but I'm not sure about dinner.'

As it turned out, however, after a long ride along the coastline, stopping at several points along the way to admire the ever-changing views, they ended up having dinner together in Carmel after all. It had been weeks since she'd had a day off, and she really did enjoy David's company.

It was a relief, too, that he didn't once press his personal interest in her. She'd told him months ago that she wasn't ready for any kind of involvement, that it was too soon after Richard's death even to consider, and ever since then he'd seemed content to be what she wanted—just a good friend.

It was almost midnight when they arrived back at the Calvert house, but still warm, with a bright, clear moon and millions of stars shining overhead in a clear, dark blue sky. They got out of the car and walked slowly together to the house.

At the door, she turned to him. 'Thanks very much, David, for a lovely day. I needed some time off more than I realised.'

'It was entirely my pleasure,' he replied. He took her hands in his and bent over to brush his lips lightly over hers. 'I won't push,' he said in a low voice. 'But you know I'm still waiting, don't you?'

She frowned. 'David...'

'No. Don't say anything. Let's just leave it like that.' He released her hands and backed away from her. 'I'll be in touch,' he said, and with a little wave headed back to the car.

When he was gone, Sheila fished her house key out of her bag and turned to unlock the door. But before she'd even inserted the key she heard someone call to her from the terrace.

'That was a tender little scene for someone who doesn't have any personal involvement.'

She whirled around to see Ross standing there, not ten feet away, a glass in his hand. As he came walking slowly towards her, she could see that he was scowling darkly.

'I don't know what you mean,' she said in some confusion.

'What I mean is that you lied to me today.'

'If you're talking about David, he's only a friend.'

He quirked a heavy dark eyebrow. 'Oh?' he drawled. 'It didn't look that way to me.'

By now she was growing rather irritated by his high-handed tone. She stared at him for some moments, wondering how best to handle the sticky situation. Although he was by no means drunk, he'd obviously been drinking.

She raised her chin at him. 'I fail to see what business it is of yours anyway,' she commented loftily. 'My personal life is my own affair.'

He thrust his face up close to hers. 'Not when you have charge of my daughter, it isn't!' he ground out. 'If you lie about one thing——'

'Now, just hold on here a minute,' she broke in angrily. 'In the first place I didn't lie to you. You can believe what you want to believe, not that it's any of your business. And in the second place, you have some nerve accusing me of dishonesty when you've been so deceitful yourself!'

He reared his head back and glared down at her. 'And just what do you mean by that? When have I ever lied to you?'

She put her hands on her hips and glared right back. 'You told me there was nothing between you and Eleanor Caldwell, yet when I called you that night at your apartment in San Francisco she answered the telephone. Just how do you explain that?'

Suddenly the incongruity of the whole situation struck her forcibly. Here they were, two people who hardly knew each other, accusing each other of deceit, their eyes locked in mortal combat—and over what? What did she care about Eleanor Caldwell? And what did he care about David Fleming? It was almost funny, and if she hadn't been so angry she would have laughed.

They stood there for several long moments, neither saying a word. Then, as she watched, the expression on his face altered slowly from outrage to something she couldn't quite identify. He bent over to set his glass on the ground, then straightened up again and took that one step towards her that separated them.

And the next thing she knew his arms had come around her, his mouth was pressed against hers, and she found herself melting against him mindlessly, drowning in his close embrace.

CHAPTER FOUR

As THE kiss deepened, Sheila's mind simply went blank. Giving herself up totally, mindlessly, to the sheer pleasure of the moment, she pressed herself closely up against his broad chest, his taut lower body and long legs. It had been so long since she'd been held in a man's arms or kissed this way that all she could do was close her eyes tightly, enjoy it and hope it never went away.

His large warm hands were moving over her back now, bare above the low bodice of her sundress, and she shivered at the sensations he was arousing in her. When she felt the tip of his tongue pressing against her lips, she uttered a sigh deep in her throat and opened them to his probing kiss.

But then, suddenly, he stiffened. His mouth left hers, and she felt him backing away from her. Bewildered by the sudden withdrawal, she looked up at him to see that he was gazing down at her with something like horror in his eyes.

'Damn you!' he growled. 'This is the last thing I wanted to happen.'

At first she was so startled and her head still in such a whirl from his ardent kiss that she couldn't think, couldn't move. She stared up at him, bewildered. Why was he so angry?

Then he smiled crookedly. 'I think you must be a witch.'

It was then that it dawned on her just what had happened. She'd been so carried away by the suddenness of it all, the thrill of his strong embrace, the taste and feel of the warm, mobile mouth on hers, that she hadn't stopped to think. She worked for this man. She was in his house to care for his daughter, not to let him make love to her.

'Come on,' he said in a firm voice. 'Let's go inside. We've got to talk and I think we both could use a drink.'

Still so confused by the strange events of the past few moments, she let him take her by the hand and lead her into the house. He made for the study, switched on a light, shut the door behind them, then made straight for the sideboard, where he poured out two glasses of Scotch.

'Here,' he said, coming back to her and handing her a glass.

She took a quick sip of the fiery liquid, and as it coursed down her throat she made a face, choked a little, and set the glass down on top of the desk. As she watched him, his head thrown back, downing half the Scotch in one long gulp, the long column of his throat working as he swallowed, she ached to go to him, to touch him, to feel his arms around her once again.

But she knew it couldn't be, and she quickly looked away. There were so many reasons against any emotional involvement with this man that her only recourse was to fight the powerful attraction she felt for him now, before it got out of hand.

When he finished his drink, he braced his lean hips back against the edge of the desk, folded his arms in front of him and gave her a wry smile. 'As

I said,' he began in a low voice, 'I didn't mean for
this to happen. But it did, and, whatever this might
be between us, for me it actually started from the
day you walked into my study, with all that bright
auburn hair and those flashing green eyes. I knew
then you were not a person I could dismiss lightly.'
His eyes narrowed. 'But it wasn't until I saw you
with your—your *friend*—today that it hit me.' He
paused and gave her an enquiring glance, as though
waiting for her to speak.

She looked at him. Out on the terrace it had been
dark, but here in the study, with the desk lamp
shining on all the familiar objects and furniture,
what had passed between them didn't seem quite
real, and her good sense gradually began to assert
itself.

'Ross,' she said slowly, 'I really think the best
thing we can do now is to forget it ever happened.'

His eyes narrowed. 'Why is that?'

'There are so many reasons. Just think about it,'
she said, spreading her arms wide. 'I work for you.
I live here in your house. My first obligation is to
Beth. I can't let anything interfere with that.'

'Oh, come now!' he said. 'That's no reason. Why
should our feelings for each other harm Beth in any
way?' He pushed himself away from the desk and
came to stand directly before her, looming over her
and glowering down at her.

She sighed in sheer exasperation. 'Ross, why are
you making this so difficult for me? You said
yourself it shouldn't have happened.'

'No,' he said carefully. 'That isn't what I said. I
said I didn't *mean* it to happen. But since it has, I
don't see how we can just dismiss it.'

'Well, I think we have to,' she said.

'And I asked you why we should.'

'I already explained to you about that,' she cried. 'What do I have to do, draw a picture?'

His mouth tightened in a grim line. 'No,' he snapped. 'All you have to do is tell me you didn't enjoy it, that you're not attracted to me.' He cocked his head to one side and gave her a cool smile. 'And if you do, you'll be lying. I know damned good and well by now when a woman is with me. And believe me, lady, you were there every step of the way.'

Her face went up in flame and she looked hurriedly away. Of course he was right. But what did he expect from her now? He continued to stand there before her, and when she glanced up at him again she saw that his expression had softened considerably.

'Shall we start over?' he asked with a smile. 'I really do think we need to talk.'

'Ross, I really don't know what we have to say to each other,' she began, but he held up a hand, stopping her.

'Just hear me out,' he said. 'What I started to tell you this afternoon before your boyfriend showed up...'

'He's *not* my boyfriend!' she exclaimed hotly. 'How many times do I have to——?'

'Well, whatever,' he commented, waving a dismissive hand in the air. 'I just wanted to explain about that night you called me at the apartment in the city. When Eleanor answered the telephone.'

'Oh, Ross, I already told you, it's not my business...'

He raised a hand to stop her. 'I know what you said, and I believe you meant it. But...' He shrugged, then gave her a slow smile. 'It's important to me what you think, and I don't want you to get the wrong idea about Eleanor and me.' He paused for a moment. 'She and Laura were buddies,' he went on slowly. 'They were a lot alike and did everything together, enjoyed the same things—parties, shopping, bridge games. They even looked alike. Anyway, when Laura died, Eleanor just sort of assumed she would step in and take her place. I've made it as clear to her as I can without insulting her that I'm not in the market, but she's a persistent type, and I've given up trying.'

'I see,' Sheila said at last. 'But I still don't know why you feel you need to tell me all this.'

'Surely there can't be any doubt in your mind by now that I'm very attracted to you,' he went on in an earnest voice. 'Actually for the first time since Laura died. And nothing will convince me that you don't feel it too.'

'Ross,' she said in a faltering voice, 'I don't know what to say. This whole thing has taken me so completely by surprise that at the moment I don't know what I think.'

'Well, maybe I'm rushing things a little. Perhaps if you told me how you felt, we might reach some meeting of the minds.'

She thought for a moment. 'Well, aside from the fact that I'm here to help Beth, and any involvement with you could jeopardise that——'

'I still don't see why,' he broke in impatiently. 'Beth loves you. How can it harm her or her progress if you and I...?' He shrugged. 'Well, we'll have to let time take care of that, won't we?' His gaze narrowed. 'But there's more to it than that, isn't there? Something more personal. You say it's not the good doctor, and I've assured you Eleanor is not a factor. What is it, then?'

She knew quite well what was really bothering her, of course. He was right. It couldn't possibly hurt Beth if she and Ross were to enter into a more personal relationship. And it was true that she was powerfully attracted to him, had been since the first day they met. What was really at the bottom of her reluctance was the fact that he didn't know her true identity. She hadn't actually deceived him, but from the moment she recognised him she had withheld information from him that could have a strong bearing on his feelings for her.

She looked away and put a hand nervously to her hair. 'I need some time, Ross,' she said at last. 'Time alone to think. And I am rather tired.'

Frowning, he raised a hand towards her as though to protest, then dropped it to his side and nodded. 'As you wish,' he replied curtly. 'I have no intention of forcing myself on you.'

With one last swift glance into the steely grey eyes, she turned and walked away from him, willing herself to go slowly, feeling his eyes on her following her, every step of the way, until she reached the hallway. She shut the door quietly behind her and leaned back against it, her eyes closed, her heart still pounding, then hurried down the hall to the safety of her own bedroom.

Sheila tossed and turned almost the entire night, trying to make sense of what had happened be-

tween her and Ross Calvert. She felt torn in a
hundred different directions. The sensations he had
stirred up in her, from just one kiss, were impossible to dismiss lightly. Even Richard hadn't af-
fected her in quite that way.

She tried to think it through rationally. According
to all indications, the great love of his life was the
dead Laura. The woman her own husband had
killed! He was attracted to her; there was no mis-
taking that. But what did he want from her? A
quick affair, right under his daughter's nose? That
would never do! And if he were ever to find out
who she really was, he'd end up hating her.

No, she decided as she finally drifted off to sleep
in the early hours of the morning. The best thing
to do was to leave, right away, before she got in
any deeper. Beth had come a long way in the past
several weeks. Some other therapist could easily
take over now. She'd just have to tell him so.

The next morning she still felt shaky. She'd have
to face him soon and get it over with, today, but
she wasn't looking forward to it. She only hoped
she'd be able to avoid him until she'd worked up
the nerve to tell him she'd decided to leave.

However, as luck would have it, she ran into him
first thing that morning on her way to breakfast.
He was coming towards her from the opposite direction, his head down, his hands shoved in the
pockets of his dark trousers, and would have
bumped into her at the kitchen door if she hadn't
stopped short and stepped aside.

He raised his head abruptly and for a brief second
their eyes met. If he was startled at the sudden en-

counter he hid it well. Smiling, he stepped back a pace to allow her to precede him through the door.

'Good morning,' he said in a casual voice. 'Sleep well?'

'Yes, thank you,' she replied stiffly, and brushed past him into the kitchen.

Mrs Swenson and Beth were already there, and from then on the conversation was dominated by the girl's chatter about her swimming progress and the apple pie she was going to help Mrs Swenson bake later that afternoon.

For the rest of the day Sheila's time was entirely taken up with Beth. The weather had turned cool, with a slight drizzle by afternoon, so that they weren't able to go swimming, but there were other equally effective forms of therapy which she could implement indoors.

Ross spent the day sequestered in his study, and by late afternoon Sheila was almost convinced that that kiss in the moonlight hadn't happened at all. Or, if so, it was only because he'd had a little too much to drink, and he was pleased at Beth's progress, grateful to her. In any case, whether he was deliberately avoiding her or really had forgotten what happened between them last night, he obviously had no intention of raising the subject with her. And that meant she wouldn't have to leave.

Early that evening she was sitting at the kitchen table shelling peas for dinner, while Mrs Swenson and Beth put the finishing touches to the apple pie, when Ross suddenly appeared at the door.

'Well, this is a cosy group,' he said with a smile as he stepped inside. He turned to the housekeeper.

'I wanted to let you know, Mrs Swenson, that I won't be dining at home tonight.'

'Oh, Daddy!' Beth cried. 'I helped make the apple pie, your favourite!'

'Sorry, honey,' he said, smoothing the girl's hair back from her forehead. 'I already promised Eleanor.'

Mrs Swenson was at the stove, just opening the oven door to put in her pie, and she turned her head slightly to give him a cold look. 'Hah!' was all she said, then slammed the door shut.

For what seemed like an eternity, no one uttered a word. Sheila kept her eyes firmly on the peas she was shelling, and, with the dead silence in the room, the steady plop, plop sound they made as they fell into the pan resounded like the reports of a gun.

'Do you have a problem with that?' Ross asked at last in a frosty tone, glaring at Mrs Swenson's back.

She turned slowly around, wiping her hands on her apron. 'Who, me?' she asked innocently. 'It's no business of mine who you spend your time with.'

'All right, then.' He turned back to Beth. 'I'll have a piece of your pie when I get home. How will that be?'

'Oh, all right, I guess.'

'Well, then,' he said. 'I'll be on my way.' He kissed the top of his daughter's head and strode out of the room without a backward glance.

From then on, his manner to Sheila become more distant with each passing day. By now it seemed clear to her that, even if he remembered the impulse that had made him reach out for her that night on the terrace, he regretted it and only wanted to make sure she didn't read any significance into it. He even seemed to be deliberately avoiding her.

Yet she could swear that from time to time she would catch him staring at her with an impenetrable look in those silvery grey eyes, watching her covertly as she sat opposite him at the dinner-table or when they happened to be in the same room for any length of time, almost as though he was about to say something to her. But he never did, and the moment always passed.

On a few occasions when she was in the pool with Beth she was certain she could see him standing in the shadows behind his study window looking out at them, but when she looked more closely no one was there.

She couldn't help feeling disappointed, let down, especially when she saw him driving off with Eleanor, but in her heart she knew it was for the best. What kind of future would she have with a man who was still grieving over the great love of his life, and, far worse, a man who would surely despise her if he ever found out who she really was?

A few weeks later on a Saturday night Ross's sister Jane came to dinner, and this time she brought her husband Howard along. He was a partner in Ross's law firm, a kindly, rather portly, balding man who was as silent as his wife was voluble.

After dinner, the two men retreated with their brandy and cigars into Ross's study to discuss the new trial, and Mrs Swenson wheeled Beth away to get her ready for bed, leaving Sheila and Jane alone in the dining-room over a last cup of coffee.

'I must say, Sheila,' Jane said with a smile, 'I'm very impressed with what you've done for Beth so far. The change in her is truly amazing. And to see her actually swimming! It's hard to believe she's the same withdrawn little mouse she'd become before you came along.'

'I'm so glad you think so, Jane,' Sheila replied. 'When you're as close to the picture as I am it's hard to see any dramatic change. But I agree with you. She has come a long way.' She took a sip of coffee, frowning. 'But I'm afraid the worst is still ahead of us, and I'm dreading it.'

'What do you mean? Surely the girl trusts you implicitly by now. Anyone can tell she adores you.'

Sheila laughed, twirling her cup around in its saucer. 'Well, I don't know if I'd go that far, but I do think I have her confidence at last.'

Jane spread her hands wide and shrugged. 'Well, then. What's the problem?'

Sheila hesitated for a moment. 'The next step isn't going to be nearly as pleasant as massage and swimming therapy,' she said slowly. 'She's got to start using those atrophied muscles, and it's going to entail some pain. Of course,' she added hurriedly, 'I won't rush her or give her more than I think she can handle at a time, but it's going to be difficult.'

'Oh, I'm sure you'll manage, Sheila. You said yourself that half the battle was getting her to trust you. Children are tougher than they appear. So long as she understands that some pain is necessary in order to walk again, she'll manage.'

'Actually,' Sheila said with a wry smile, 'I'm not nearly as worried about Beth as I am her father.' She shrugged. 'He's not going to like it.'

'Oh, bother Ross!' Jane exclaimed with a wave of her hand. 'He'll just have to take his lumps, like everyone else. Besides, he'll be leaving for the new trial soon.'

'I know. I hope you're right.'

The two women sat in silence then for several moments, each absorbed in her own thoughts. The sun had set about half an hour ago, and the sky was filled with brilliant colour, radiant streaks of red and gold that were reflected on the calm sea.

Sheila sat gazing out at the lovely sight through the open French doors that led to the terrace until she became uncomfortably aware of Jane's eyes upon her. When she turned to give her a questioning look, Jane glanced hastily away, apparently at a loss for words for the first time since Sheila had known her.

After a moment Jane cleared her throat noisily. 'Other than that,' she began hesitantly, 'I mean your concern over Ross's reaction to Beth's future therapy—how are things between you and my brother?'

Sheila could feel her face redden. 'Oh, fine,' she said with an offhand lift of her shoulders. 'Although we don't see much of each other. He's gone a great deal.'

Jane set her mouth in a thin line of disapproval. 'So I've heard,' was the dry comment. 'I take it you're referring to Eleanor Caldwell?'

'Well, partly,' Sheila replied. 'And then he's very involved with his work.'

'That woman is a damned pest!' Jane exploded. She got up from her chair and went over to the sideboard to pour herself a glass of brandy. 'How about you?' she asked, holding up the bottle.

'No. No, thanks,' Sheila replied. 'I'm fine with coffee.'

Jane returned to her seat, took a long sip of brandy, then set her glass down on the table and gave Sheila a piercing look. 'Let me tell you a little about Eleanor Caldwell,' she began in a tight even tone. 'For one thing, she's had her eye on my brother ever since she and her husband—ex-husband now—moved in up the road. Oh, I'm not saying she ever did anything about it, especially when Laura was alive. But even an old fogey like me could see that she was letting Ross know from the day they met that she was available if he wanted to take the trouble.'

Sheila gave her a troubled look. 'But from what I've gathered she and Laura were best friends!' she objected. 'How could she expect——?'

'I can see you don't know dear Eleanor,' Jane broke in. 'Of course she could see from day one that it wasn't a happy marriage.' Suddenly her eyes widened and she clasped a hand over her mouth. 'Oh, dear,' she wailed. 'Big-mouth Jane has put her foot in it again.'

Although her regret at the harsh words seemed genuine, Sheila could have sworn she'd made the comment about Ross's marriage on purpose, that for some reason Jane had wanted her to know that it was not as blissful as Sheila had assumed.

'But I thought——' she began.

'Listen,' Jane said, interrupting again and putting a hand over Sheila's. 'I probably shouldn't have said anything, but I've suspected for some time now—call it an informed hunch—that my brother is far more interested in you as a woman than as Beth's therapist. Not that he'd ever let on to me, of course. He still feels so guilty over Laura's death that he's been punishing himself ever since.'

'Guilty!' Sheila cried. 'But why should he feel guilty? The accident wasn't his fault!' Then, realising she'd said too much, she added weakly, 'Was it?'

'Of course not!' Jane replied heatedly. 'Some drunken idiot ran into them. Killed himself, too, if memory serves me correctly.' She shook her head. 'No, Ross feels guilty because of what was going on before the accident.'

'What do you mean?'

'I mean that whatever love had been between him and Laura died long before the accident. He never said anything to me, of course. And neither did she.'

Sheila was stunned. All she could do was stare at Jane, wide-eyed, speechless. The lovely picture she had painted in her mind of the perfect marriage, the love between them, the grief Ross still felt for his adored wife, all went flying out the window, and she couldn't quite take it all in.

'Then what makes you think . . . ?' she sputtered at last.

'Well, for one thing, Laura refused to have any more children after Beth was born; said it would ruin her figure. And she was the one who insisted on getting that apartment in the city.' She snorted.

'She spent more time there than she did here. And I don't think it was alone.'

Jane sighed then and rose slowly to her feet. 'I'd better quit while I'm ahead,' she remarked drily. 'I've already said far more than I should, and if you ever repeat what I've told you I'll deny the whole thing.' Then she smiled. 'The only reason I mentioned any of this to you, Sheila, is that I know my brother. I'm not blind to the way he looks at you, the longing in his eyes. I think you could be just the one to make him forget.

'Now,' she said brusquely, gathering up her handbag from the sideboard, 'I'll see if I can drag Howard away from the study. It's time we were heading home.'

Jane's revelations about Ross's dead wife and their marriage had opened up a world of possibilities to Sheila. Not to mention Jane's comments about his interest in her, Sheila. For the next few days it was all she could think about.

She began to see him with entirely new eyes—and to notice things she hadn't really taken in before, or at most only vaguely suspected. He did seem to be watching her covertly, and from time to time she could have sworn he was about to speak to her.

But, she kept reminding herself sternly whenever her idle thoughts strayed in that direction, Ross Calvert was not the reason she was in his home. She'd come to help his daughter walk again. Beth was her first priority, and the time had come to intensify her therapy. She really had made re-

markable progress, but so far it had all been rela-
tively painless, even fun.

The next step, however, would not be so
pleasant—and in fact it turned out to be even worse
than she'd feared. Although Beth trusted her by
now and was anxious to co-operate, a whole year
of misguided indulgence by a doting, guilt-ridden
father wasn't going to be undone in the space of a
few weeks.

One afternoon, in the privacy of the old nursery,
which had been set up as a therapy-room, Sheila
pushed the girl as far as she dared, and got absolutely nowhere. No matter how patient she was, or
how insistent that Beth try to walk, she couldn't
get her to take that first step.

'I said I'd never lie to you, Beth,' she said. 'And
I told you it was going to hurt a little at first. Come
on, now, be a brave girl. I'm right here beside you.
If you start to fall, I'll catch you. Now, let's try
one more time.'

To give the girl credit, she did try, but the moment
she put that extra weight on the worn muscles of
her legs in an attempt to walk she would stop cold,
paralysed by her fear of pain. When the tears came,
Sheila knew it was time to back off.

'All right,' she said at last with a smile, gathering
the girl up in her arms and settling her in her wheelchair. 'We won't do any more today. Maybe
tomorrow we can try again. Now, it's a beautiful
day. How about a quick swim before dinner?'

Luckily Ross was so involved these days with his
upcoming trial that at least he wasn't hovering
around on the sidelines monitoring every move she
made. She'd warned him that it would be necessary

to get past that barrier of fear, and he had agreed
with her. She knew, however, that it was only lip-
service and that the moment he saw those tears in
Beth's eyes he'd weaken and interfere.

Late that night, Sheila was awakened out of a deep
sleep by the sound of muffled cries coming from
the room next to hers—Beth's room. Groggily, she
raised her head and glanced at the luminous dial
of the clock on the table beside her bed. It was past
two o'clock in the morning!

When the cries came again, louder this time, she
hurriedly slipped out of bed, dashed out into the
corridor and opened the door of Beth's bedroom.
A shaft of moonlight was streaking in through the
open window, and in its glow she could see the girl
sitting bolt upright in her narrow bed, her eyes wide
with fear, a cry just dying on her lips.

'Beth!' she cried, rushing to her side. 'What is
it?' She sat down beside her and held her arms out.
'Did you have a bad dream? There now, it'll be all
right.'

The girl was sobbing by now, but as Sheila
smoothed the damp hair back from her forehead,
murmuring soothing words, she gradually began to
quieten down. At least the panic seemed to be over,
and before long the heart-rending sobs had dis-
solved into sniffles.

Then, suddenly, Sheila became aware of a
looming presence at the door. She turned her head
to see Ross standing there. He was wearing a dark
robe, tied loosely at the waist, his black hair tousled,
his face stricken. He stood there for a moment, one

hand raised, then strode directly to the side of the bed.

Sheila groaned inwardly. All she needed was to have Ross barging in just when she got the girl settled. He'd spoil everything.

'What is it?' he asked in a low, tense voice. 'What happened?'

'Nothing,' Sheila replied quickly. 'She just had a bad dream. It's all right now. Please go. She's fine.'

But the minute Beth heard his voice she pulled away from Sheila and broke into renewed sobbing. 'Oh, Daddy!' she cried, holding out her arms to him. 'She made it hurt.'

'There, there, darling,' he murmured, lifting her up and clutching her tightly. 'Never mind. It's only a dream.'

Sheila got up from the bed and walked slowly over to the door, then stood there for a moment, pondering the sticky situation. She needed to have this out with Ross now, tonight, before it could be forgotten. She watched as he finally eased the girl back down in her bed, tucked the covers up around her neck and leaned over to kiss her goodnight.

When he finally turned around to face Sheila, his eyes were stern and accusing. Then, after one last glance at Beth, who seemed to have fallen asleep instantly, as children do, he began to walk slowly towards her. Sheila folded her arms across her chest and lifted her chin. She wasn't going to back down an inch.

'Come on,' he muttered as he moved past her. 'We need to talk.'

'Yes,' she agreed grimly. 'We certainly do.'

   She followed him out into the hall, shut the door
quietly behind her and turned to face him.
   'What was all that about?' he demanded gruffly.
   'I told you. It was only a bad dream.'
   'Something must have brought it on. She hasn't
had a nightmare for months. What did she mean
when she said you'd hurt her?'
   'I tried to step up her therapy a little today, and
she wasn't ready for it.'
   The grey eyes blazed at her. 'I thought you were
supposed to be the professional. Shouldn't you have
known it was too soon?'
   'How could I,' she shot back at him, 'until I
tried?' She sighed in exasperation. 'Ross, I explained all this to you the day I got here,' she went
on with elaborate patience. 'It's quite simple. Either
you trust me or you don't. And I'm telling you that
if you want Beth to walk again, to live a normal
life, she's going to have to suffer a little. I know
it's hard for you, and I'll take it as easily and slowly
as I can, but the simple fact is it must be done.'
   He opened his mouth, his brow still like thunder,
but stopped short. He frowned, then rubbed a hand
slowly over the back of his neck, glaring down at
the floor.
   She raised a hand towards him. 'Believe me,
Ross, I promise I'll do my best to make it as painless
as possible, but if you show up offering sympathy
every time it gets rough you only give her a way
out of what must be done. That only weakens her.
What she needs most of all right now is courage.'
   He raised his eyes. 'And you think you can give
her that?'
   'I can try. It's my job, after all.'

'I don't know,' he said, shaking his head. 'It's just that I can't bear to see her hurt.'

'I know,' she said softly. All the anger had drained out of her by now, and her heart went out to him.

Then, suddenly, it was all too much for her. Somehow Beth's bad dream, the angry scene with Ross had touched her on her own painful memories—of the accident, the death of her husband, the weeks she had spent in the hospital, the slow struggle back to health. With a strangled sob she couldn't quite fight down, she put her hands over her face and turned away from him.

'Sheila,' she heard him call to her in a low voice. 'What is it?'

One hand came to rest tentatively on her shoulder. Shaking herself free, she started to run away from him, but he grasped her firmly so that she wasn't able to move. Slowly, he turned her around to face him. He gazed down at her stricken face for a brief second, then put his arms around her and gathered her to him.

CHAPTER FIVE

With a little sigh, Sheila sank against the tall, strong body and made her mind go blank. In spite of all her good resolutions about the importance of keeping her relationship with Ross Calvert on an impersonal plane, she was simply powerless at that moment to resist the spell he had cast over her. He made her feel so safe, so protected and cared for.

In fact, until he came along she hadn't begun to realise just how lonely she'd been since Richard's death, nor just how wonderful it could be to feel a man's arms around her once again. His hands were warm on her bare shoulders and back, the gentle stroking, the low, murmuring sounds he made so soothing that her tears soon subsided into inglorious sniffles.

She tried to stifle them, but since her nose was dripping badly by now there wasn't much else she could do. Then she felt Ross's body shaking against hers and heard his low chuckle.

She pulled her head back and looked up at him. 'I don't see what's so funny.'

'Sorry,' he said quickly. He drew the corners of his mouth down and wrinkled his forehead in an expression of mock-sympathy.

She ran the back of her hand over her damp eyes and reached for one of the tissues she always kept in the pocket of her robe. Her robe! Where was her robe? It dawned on her then that in her haste to get to Beth she hadn't even thought to put it on and was standing there wearing nothing but a thin nightgown.

Flushing deeply, she gazed up at Ross, who was reaching into the pocket of his own dark robe, the grin back on his face. At least *he'd* had the presence of mind not to come dashing out here half naked, except, she realised on closer inspection, the loosely tied robe did expose a rather nice view of his smooth masculine chest.

'Here,' he said, handing her a clean handkerchief. 'Be my guest.'

She didn't now whether to laugh or cry, but in the end she had to smile. She took the handkerchief from him and wiped her eyes, then turned away to give her nose a thorough blow. When she turned back to him the smile had faded from his lips, and the silvery grey eyes were glittering down at her, no longer in amusement or concern, but in an expression that she recognised immediately as one of naked desire.

She hurriedly crossed her arms in front of her, but as their eyes locked together she knew it was far too late for that. He reached out a hand and put it on her face, his long fingers tracing the line of her jaw, her mouth, her chin. She drew in a quick gasping breath at the touch, knowing she should leave, now, before it was too late, but unable to move a step away from him.

'Sheila,' he said in a low voice. The hand on her face slid around to the back of her neck and she felt herself being pulled slowly towards him.

She opened her mouth to protest, but before she could get a word out he had gathered her into his arms and pressed his lips firmly down upon hers. With a low groan deep in her throat, Sheila let her head fall back and gave herself up to the utter sweetness of his kiss.

As though spurred on by this sign of her surrender, his embrace rapidly became more urgent, more demanding. His mouth opened wider, and one hand moved to the base of her throat, lingered there for a moment, then gradually began to slide lower until it came to rest at the lacy border of her low-cut nightgown.

In the utter silence, she could hear only the heavy rasp of his breathing—or was it her own? It didn't matter. By now the hand at her throat had slid beneath the filmy bodice, his fingers stroking the bare flesh beneath it, tantalising her with the promise of more to come. Waves of heat were sweeping over her, singing in her bloodstream.

Just then a high, piping voice broke the stillness. 'Daddy! Daddy! Where are you?' Beth cried from the bedroom.

Ross immediately jerked his head up. He stood there for a moment, stock-still, his ears cocked, obviously shaken, his eyes narrowed, listening. When the cry came again, he dropped his hands from Sheila, swivelled around and strode towards the bedroom.

Sheila stood in the hallway, shivering, and listening to the low murmur of voices coming from inside, uncertain what she should do now. For a brief moment she was tempted to follow him, but then thought better of it. There was nothing she could do. She turned and began slowly walking away towards her own room.

Lying in bed, restless and uneasy, tossing and turning, she relived the short scene in the hallway with Ross over and over again. His kiss, the touch of his hands, the feel of his hard body against hers. It had been a magical moment with a powerful effect on her. Clearly on Ross as well.

But wasn't it just as well they'd been interrupted before it was too late and they'd taken an irrevocable step? Although what had happened tonight was clear evidence of the powerful attraction that simmered between them just below the surface, she knew quite well that there couldn't possibly be any future in it. Not only was her professional role in his house against it, but the events of the past, the accident that had killed his wife and crippled his daughter, made it impossible.

He must never find out that it had been her dead husband who caused that accident. It would not only destroy her effectiveness with Beth, but make him hate her. She couldn't tell him the truth, and there was certainly no hope for a relationship based on a lie.

The next morning, after a late solitary breakfast, Sheila made her way to the therapy-room with a growing sense of anxiety. After yesterday's utter failure with Beth, she'd have to be very cautious in her approach today.

Perhaps she *had* pushed the girl too hard, as her father seemed to believe. The nightmare could be an indication that he was right.

She paused for a moment when she arrived at the door, still trying to make up her mind what to do. She'd just have to play it by ear, rely on her instincts. Perhaps the girl wouldn't even show up today.

But when she opened the door, Beth was there, sitting in her wheelchair by the window. And, she noticed with a heartfelt sigh of relief, she'd come alone. Although the girl's eyes were wide with apprehension and she seemed to be shrinking as far as possible back into her chair, at least she'd worked up the courage to come at all.

'Good morning, Beth,' she called in a cheerful voice as she walked towards her. 'How are you feeling today?'

She stopped short some distance away from the chair so as to appear as non-threatening as possible, but even so the expression on the girl's face was still wary.

'All right,' she replied in a small voice.

'No more bad dreams?'

Beth shook her head, then blurted out in a rush, 'Is it going to hurt today?'

Sheila's heart went out to her. Although she had long since learned the crucial importance of keeping an emotional distance from her small patients, she couldn't help being deeply moved by the terror she saw in the girl's eyes. She knew what she had to do.

She knelt down beside the chair and put an arm around the thin shoulders. 'No,' she said in a low, soothing voice. 'It's not going to hurt today. In fact,' she went on brightly, 'you were such a brave girl to come back this morning all by yourself that we're going to take a little break. It's a beautiful day. How about a swim?'

The girl brightened immediately. 'Oh, yes!' she cried.

Sheila rose to her feet. 'All right, let's go get ready. I'll help you get your swimsuit on.' She hesitated a moment. 'But you know, Beth, we're going to have to try again soon to get those leg muscles working, and that means it's going to hurt.'

Beth's smile faded and she gazed up wordlessly at Sheila, her eyes clouding over again.

'You do want to walk again, don't you, Beth?' Sheila went on. 'To run and play like other children?'

'Yes,' Beth said slowly at last. 'But not today.'

Sheila had to laugh. 'No. Not today.'

They stayed in the pool for two hours, laughing and playing. Beth was getting to be like a little fish in the water, fearless now even of the deep end. Since any exercise at all was good for her, Sheila didn't consider the morning wasted.

She only hoped she'd done the right thing by easing off at this point. Treating frightened children was difficult enough to begin with. Dealing with a fond parent's protective instincts made it doubly so. And when there was a personal involvement with that parent clouding her mind, it became almost impossible.

Was she delaying the painful therapy for Beth's sake? Or her father's? The memory of their late-night encounter outside Beth's room still haunted her. Of course, nothing had really happened. Well, nothing much. But it could have, very easily, if Beth hadn't called out for him at just that moment.

She was walking a tightrope here, and wasn't at all sure she could keep her balance. What she needed was some professional advice. And to stay as far away as possible from that disturbing man.

That afternoon, while Beth was taking her nap and Mrs Swenson was shut up in her room with her beloved soap operas, Sheila went into the kitchen to use the telephone.

As she passed by Ross's study, she stopped for a moment, listening for signs of life behind the closed door. She hadn't seen him at all that day. Apparently he was working hard on his new case, even taking his meals in there.

It could be that he was also going out of his way to avoid her after last night. He must be as aware as she how necessary it was to keep a safe distance between them while the therapy was in progress, especially since they disagreed so basically on the course that that therapy should take.

In the kitchen she dialled Kate's number, and after a few rings she answered in her usual abrupt tones. 'Kate O'Neill here.'

'Kate, it's Sheila.'

'Well, Sheila!' Kate exclaimed loudly. 'Believe it or not I was just about to call you! How's the job going?'

'Well, to tell you the truth, I seem to have run into a few problems,' Sheila replied cautiously.

'Problems? What problems?' Kate demanded. 'That doesn't sound like you at all.'

'I know. That's why I called. I hate to bother you. I know how busy you are. But I could use some free advice if you have the time.'

'Now isn't a good time,' Kate replied. 'I'm due at a meeting of the hospital board in a few minutes. Still trying to squeeze a bigger budget out of them for the children's therapy programme. Can I call you back later?'

Sheila thought for a minute. 'I don't know, Kate. Later could be too late. I don't have a telephone in my bedroom, and we need privacy for what I want to discuss with you. I don't suppose I could talk you into driving down and having dinner with me this evening? We could meet in Monterey.'

'Sounds great. How about that little Italian restaurant overlooking the ocean? About seven o'clock?'

'That would be perfect.'

'All right. I'll see you then. Now, I have to run if I'm going to get to my meeting on time.'

'Right. And thanks, Kate.'

The popular little restaurant was crowded when Sheila arrived that evening, and she congratulated herself that she had made reservations beforehand. Kate was already at their table, a martini in hand, when Sheila sat down opposite her.

After the greetings were over, Kate gave her a long appraising look over her cocktail. 'Well, I must say, Sheila, for a girl with problems, you're looking well. In fact, you're glowing.' She gave an abrupt laugh. 'What's more, if I didn't know you better, I'd say there was a man in the picture.' She finished her drink and raised her hand for the waitress to bring her another. 'Now, what's your big problem?'

'Actually,' Sheila replied, flushing a little, 'you've already hit on it.' She smiled at her friend. 'You always did have an unerring eye for the truth.'

Kate's eyes flew open. 'You don't mean...?'

Sheila sighed. 'I'd better start at the beginning.'

While they sipped their drinks, then later over a delicious dinner of scampi and ravioli, Sheila told Kate the whole story—how she'd recognised Ross right away, been tempted not to take the job, then somehow decided to stay after all.

'And you mean to say in all this time he hasn't connected you with the accident at all?'

Sheila shrugged. 'Apparently not. But then, how could he? I mean, I was using my married name then. My face was covered with bandages from all that surgery.' She paused to take a sip of after-dinner coffee. 'But that's not the problem.'

Kate leaned back in her chair and lit a cigarette. 'No,' she said, blowing out smoke. 'I can see that. So you've gone and fallen for your boss.' She shook her head slowly from side to side. 'I'm surprised at you, Sheila. I'd never have thought you would allow your personal feelings to interfere with your work.' Her tone was severe, but there was a hint of a playful smile hovering about her lips that softened the harsh words.

'Oh, don't think I haven't told myself that a million times,' Sheila groaned. 'The question is, what do I do about it? Sometimes I'm convinced I should quit the job, just get out, but I really have made good progress with Beth, and I'm afraid that changing therapists now, after I've gained her trust, would only set her back.'

'Yes, I can see that.' Kate hesitated a moment, then said in an offhand tone, 'I take it Ross Calvert returns your interest?'

Sheila coloured deeply. 'Well, yes, apparently so.'

'How far has it gone?'

'Not very,' Sheila hedged.

Kate slowly ground out her cigarette, frowning down at the mess she was making in the ashtray. 'Of course,' she went on, giving Sheila a stern look, 'the answer is really quite simple.'

'Oh, really?' Sheila said in a dry tone. 'Tell me about it.'

Kate shrugged. 'Basically, there's only one issue at stake here: your patient's welfare. The highest priority must be what's best for her.'

Sheila spread her arms wide in sheer frustration. 'Don't you think I know that? The problem is that my mind is so muddled by now, I can't seem to decide any more what *is* best for her.'

Kate wagged a finger at her. 'Listen, my dear, you may be fuddled by this romantic hero of yours, but at heart you're a professional, with all the right instincts. It's just not in you to do anything—*anything*!—that will jeopardise that girl's recovery.'

'Oh, Kate, I hope you're right. The trouble is that Ross keeps interfering; he thinks I'm being too hard on Beth when I push her.'

Kate laughed. 'Well, that's normal. All parents are that way. You've had to deal with it constantly in the past.'

'Yes, but what I'm afraid of is that I'll do what he wants and ease up on the therapy, just to keep him happy.'

Kate shook her head vigorously. 'No. You won't do that. You're worrying over nothing, Sheila. It sounds to me as though you've been handling the case perfectly.' She paused for a moment. 'Actually, I think you have a more serious problem on your hands.'

Sheila gave her a startled look. 'What's that?'

Kate leaned forward and looked directly into her eyes. 'If it's true that Ross Calvert is as attracted to you as you are to him, there's no telling where that could lead, once the girl is well again.'

Sheila looked down at her hands. 'Perhaps,' she murmured. 'I hadn't really thought that far ahead.'

'Well, my dear, I think you'd better. What's going to happen when he finds out who you are?'

'I don't know,' Sheila replied miserably. 'And don't think I haven't agonised over that little problem myself.'

'Wouldn't it be better if you told him now?' Kate asked softly.

Sheila shook her head slowly from side to side, then gave her friend a stricken look. 'I don't know,' she replied in a low voice. 'I just can't bring myself to do it. Not yet.'

'I hate to sound like a wet blanket, but the longer you put it off, the harder it will be in the long run.' She rose from her chair. 'Now, I really must be going.' She put a hand on Sheila's shoulder and gave it a little squeeze. 'Call me and let me know how things work out.'

Sheila glanced up at her with a weak smile. 'Yes, of course. And thanks for coming down. And listening.'

*   *   *

Later that evening, back at the house, as Sheila passed by the living-room she glanced inside to see Ross and Beth sitting together on the sofa watching television. Although the talk with Kate had cleared up much of her confusion, she wasn't in the mood to face either of them tonight, and she hurried by the open doorway on her way to her own room.

But Beth had already spotted her. 'Oh, Sheila,' she called out as she passed by. 'There you are. Come and watch with us. It's a programme all about cats and lions and tigers.'

Sheila stopped and poked her head inside, forcing out a smile. 'Oh, not tonight, Beth. I think I'll turn in early.'

Beth giggled. 'Daddy said you probably had a date tonight with your doctor friend. Did you?'

'Oh, something like that,' Sheila replied. She stood there for a moment awkwardly, not daring to meet Ross's eye, but somehow certain that that steely gaze was fixed firmly on her. 'I'll say good-night now. See you tomorrow.'

Let him think I had a date with David, she decided as she got ready for bed. Kate was right. Her first duty was to Beth. She should have known better than to get personally involved with a patient's father in the first place, and she'd been the worst kind of a fool to let it go as far as it had. It was definitely time to put a stop to it.

Still, when it dawned on her in the next few days that Ross seemed to have come to the same conclusion, her relief was oddly mingled with a sense of disappointment. He spent most of his time in the study, but, living in the same house, they could hardly avoid each other completely. Although he

always rose very early and breakfasted alone, they
usually all had dinner together in the evening.

At these times, by tacit mutual consent, they
treated each other with distant courtesy, their conversation confined to, 'Would you please pass the
potatoes?' or, 'Would you care for another glass
of wine?'

In time this became very wearing on her, and as
she watched him covertly at the dinner-table, or
sitting with Beth in the evening, she sensed that he
seemed to be feeling the strain as much as she was.
The little creases at the corners of his eyes were
etched more deeply, his face looked drawn, and his
speech, while always polite, grew more curt with
each passing day.

She continued to hold back on pushing Beth's
therapy, not only because she needed to regain the
girl's trust more completely, but also because, with
her over-protective father in the same house, she
was afraid that any sign of pain would bring him
running to the girl's rescue.

She debated endlessly whether that decision was
based on what was best for the girl or on her fear
of antagonising Ross, but couldn't seem to resolve
it. On the principle 'When in doubt, do nothing,'
she just let it slide. She did continue with the mas-
sages and stretching exercises and swimming, but
didn't insist that Beth try to walk again. Ross should
be leaving for his new trial soon, and she could
intensify the therapy when he was safely out of the
house.

The weather continued fine, and she and Beth
spent hours in the pool each day. She had de-
veloped a deep tan from being out in the sun so

much, and her rich auburn hair had become bleached into a much lighter streaky colour.

On one especially warm morning in early June, Ross, who had apparently slept later than usual, ate his breakfast with Beth and Sheila. After serving them all batches of blueberry pancakes, Mrs Swenson had gone to the stove to brew a fresh pot of coffee. Beth was chattering about a cartoon programme she had watched on television, and as usual Ross and Sheila treated each other with polite deference and cool reserve.

Beth was obviously overjoyed to be having breakfast with her father, and, because of the late hour, immediately assumed he was giving himself a holiday from his labours.

'Now you can go swimming with us today,' she said happily. 'You haven't seen me do the backstroke. Sheila taught me.'

Ross gave her a rather weary smile and shook his head. 'Not today, sweetheart,' he said. 'I have some errands to run in town...' But he stopped short when he saw Beth's face fall, the tears gather in her eyes.

'But Daddy, you haven't come to watch me swim for ages.' She turned to Sheila, who had kept her eyes glued firmly on her plate throughout the entire exchange. 'Tell him, Sheila, how well I can do the backstroke now.'

'Well, Beth, if your father doesn't feel he can spare the time, then...'

'I didn't say that!' she heard him bark all of a sudden.

Startled, she glanced up at him. His face was livid, his eyes flashing, his mouth working soundlessly, and he was obviously very angry. She opened her mouth to explain that she didn't mean to criticise him in any way, but just then he rose abruptly from his chair, almost knocking it over backwards in the process, and threw his napkin down on the table. Then, sucking in a deep lungful of air, as though struggling to gain control of himself, he put a hand on Beth's shoulder. 'Of course I want to see you do the backstroke, Beth,' he said in a gentler tone. He gave her a forced smile. 'In fact I wouldn't miss it.' He flashed a glowering look at Sheila. 'I can always run my errands later.'

'Oh, goody,' cried the girl, totally oblivious to the fraught undercurrents. 'And you'll have to get your swimming-trunks on and go in with us.' She turned to Sheila. 'Won't he?'

Sheila only murmured something non-committal. By now Ross wasn't paying the least attention to her anyway. He had grasped the handles of Beth's chair and was already wheeling her towards the door.

When they were gone, Sheila sat motionless for a few seconds, still stunned by the tense little scene. What on earth had been wrong with him? What had she said to make him so angry? And that anger was quite obviously aimed directly at her.

Then, from the direction of the stove, she heard Mrs Swenson clear her throat loudly. Darting her a quick glance, Sheila noticed that her mouth was twitching with suppressed laughter, her blue eyes sparkling with amusement, her brows raised meaningfully.

'Well!' she exclaimed, arms akimbo. 'I wonder what burr got under *his* tail!'

Sheila had to laugh, knowing she shouldn't, but unable to help herself. It *had* been rather funny, the look on his face. And all over a simple request to go swimming.

She shook her head and rose slowly to her feet. 'Who knows, where men are concerned?'

She took much longer than usual getting her swimming costume on, hoping that he'd have cooled off by the time she went to join them in the pool. Before setting off, she gave herself a rueful glance in the mirror. She still hadn't bought the new swimsuit, as she'd intended. The tank suit was not only dowdy, but had a tendency to cling in all the wrong places when it was wet. So long as Ross would be in the pool watching Beth, maybe she could just sit on the sidelines today. Even keep a towel draped over her.

He and Beth were both already in the water when she arrived. Beth was performing an awkward backstroke for him, while he hovered at her side every inch of the way. Whatever had been eating at him at breakfast seemed to have dissipated, and his face was beaming down at his daughter with the first sign of real joy Sheila had seen on it for days.

'Look at me! Look at me!' the girl cried the moment she spotted Sheila.

Sheila smiled and waved, then sat down on a lounger by the side of the pool. 'You're doing great!' she called to her.

She sat there watching for a while, trying her best to keep her eyes off Ross as he bent over Beth, but somehow they kept straying to the tall man—the broad expanse of bare masculine chest, the broad muscular shoulders, the strong arms. She fidgeted in her chair, changing her position several times, but the lure of that splendid figure was too much for her wayward gaze.

Finally, she jumped to her feet. With Ross here hovering so protectively over his daughter, there was really no need for her presence. Just then, however, Beth came paddling over to the side of the pool and called to her.

'Aren't you coming in, Sheila? The water is so nice.' She turned to Ross. 'Daddy, tell Sheila to come in.'

Without thinking, Sheila glanced over at him. Their eyes met briefly, then in the next instant they both looked hurriedly away at the same time.

'I can't make her come in if she doesn't want to, Beth,' he explained patiently.

'But we need her for our ball game,' Beth protested. 'Please, Sheila,' she begged. 'Come and play with us.'

Things were escalating out of proportion by now, and Sheila decided the best way to handle the sticky situation was just to get in the pool and be done with it. After all, nothing very dramatic could happen out here in broad daylight with Beth there to monitor their every move.

Slipping the towel off her shoulders, she picked up the bright red beach ball lying at the edge of the pool and jumped into the water with a loud splash.

'Here,' she called to Beth, raising the ball high up above her head. 'Catch.'

With a loud shriek, Beth reached out for the ball as it came sailing her way. It slipped out of her hands immediately, but with Ross's help she soon retrieved it and tossed it back to Sheila.

From then on, with Ross and Sheila taking turns holding Beth, they became involved in a hilarious game of catch. After a time, when Sheila saw how Beth's eyes sparkled with the sheer joy of play, and heard her infectious giggles, she forgot her own anxiety.

Ross too seemed to be more relaxed than she'd seen him in days. The worry-lines on his forehead were smoothed out, the corners of his eyes crinkled with pleasure at his daughter's joy, and he was almost boyish in his total concentration on the silly game.

At one point, Beth threw the ball at Sheila with all her strength, and it hit her square on the forehead, sending her backwards under the water. When she emerged, gasping and spluttering, all three broke into gales of laughter.

'I'm going to get you for that, young lady,' she called as she retrieved the ball.

At that point, Ross was standing behind Beth, supporting her around the waist with his arms. As Sheila raised the ball over her head to throw it at Beth, the laughter suddenly died on his lips, and the grey eyes glazed over as they dropped downwards. Flustered, immediately aware of what had caught his attention in the thin wet swimsuit, Sheila gave the ball a quick throw, then dipped down beneath the surface of the water, her face burning.

Just then a woman's voice called out. 'Well, isn't this is a cosy little scene?'

All three heads turned to see Eleanor Caldwell striding down the path from the house. She was wearing a terry-cloth robe, her sleek blonde hair was pinned up loosely on top of her head, and she had on a fashionably oversized pair of dark glasses.

She stood at the edge of the pool for a few seconds, her hands on her hips, a too bright smile on her face, staring down at the silent little group in the water.

'Mind if I join you?' she finally drawled.

Without waiting for a reply, she shrugged off her robe and threw it on a nearby *chaise-longue*, then stepped to the edge of the pool and stood there for a second, hands on hips, as though posing.

For a moment, Sheila didn't think she was wearing anything at all, but on closer look she could see that indeed Eleanor did have on a suit—of sorts—a flesh-coloured bikini that barely concealed all the important parts of her anatomy. Of course, with her full figure and statuesque height, she looked like a million dollars, and Sheila thought of her own shabby tank suit with a pang of dismay.

In the next moment, Eleanor had dived gracefully into the deep end of the pool and was swimming towards them in long, smooth strokes. She stopped just inches short of Ross, who was still holding Beth. The minute Eleanor surfaced, however, the girl wriggled out of his grasp and swam over to Sheila.

'Good grief, Beth!' Eleanor called to her. 'You're like a little fish!' She flashed a brilliant smile up at Ross. 'It's remarkable the progress she's made.'

'Yes,' he said. 'Thanks to Sheila.'

Eleanor turned around so that she was facing Ross and put a hand on his face. 'Oh, Ross, I'm so happy for you,' she burbled.

'If she gets any closer,' Sheila muttered to herself, 'she'll be behind him.' Turning to Beth, she gathered her up in her arms. Holding on to her tightly, to cover the embarrassing tank suit, she set her down on the edge of the pool, then started to climb out.

'Oh, you're not leaving, are you?' Eleanor called. 'Not on my account, I hope.'

'Oh, no,' Sheila replied, wrapping a towel around Beth and settling her in the wheelchair. 'I think Beth has had enough for today. It's almost time for her lunch.'

She had expected a storm of protest from the girl herself, but instead she seemed oddly acquiescent about the abrupt end of their game. She really was, Sheila assured herself as she threw her own towel around her shoulders and started pushing the chair up the path towards the house. It wasn't just an excuse to leave.

At the door to the kitchen, she couldn't resist turning around for one last glance at the pool. Eleanor had her arms around Ross's neck by now, and although his own arms remained hanging loosely at his sides he didn't look as though he was suffering from her attentions.

With a little snort, Sheila turned on her heel and wheeled Beth into the house.

CHAPTER SIX

THAT evening after dinner, Sheila took a short walk around the grounds in the late dusk. It had been a lovely day, and the shadows were just beginning to fall, the sky turning a darker blue. When she came back to the house she stayed out on the terrace for some time, leaning over the balustrade and gazing out at the gently rolling sea.

Beth had gone to bed and Mrs Swenson was settled in her own room in front of the television. She was quite alone, enjoying the sensation of solitude, the warm evening breeze, the scent of the roses wafting up from the garden below. Then suddenly she heard footsteps coming up behind her.

'Mind if I join you?' came Ross's voice.

Quickly, she swivelled her head around. 'N-no,' she stammered. 'Of course not.'

It was the first time they had been alone since the night of Beth's nightmare, two weeks ago, and a heated sensation had already begun to course through her at his nearness.

He came up to her and they stood silently side by side for some moments, looking out into the gathering dusk. He was wearing a short-sleeved knit shirt, standing only inches away from her now, and she could almost feel the skin of his bare arm against hers, unsettling her, filling her with a yearning she couldn't fight down.

Finally, he turned to her. 'I want to apologise to you for snapping at you the way I did at breakfast this morning.'

She gave him a quick smile. 'Oh, no need for that. You've been working hard, and we all have our off-days. I only hope you realise that I didn't mean anything by my remark about not sparing the time to go swimming with Beth. I know how deeply you care for her.'

'Yes,' he said. 'And I was wrong to take your comment any other way. It's just that——' He broke off, and stood there for a moment staring down at his hands in brooding silence. Then he glanced over at her again. 'I also wanted to thank you for joining in the game with Beth in the pool today. It meant a lot to her.'

'Oh, it was fun,' she replied quickly. 'And wonderful to see how much she was enjoying herself.'

'Yes,' he replied in a grimmer tone. 'We all were. Until that pest Eleanor showed up and threw a spanner in the works.'

Sheila didn't dare move a muscle for fear of letting the intense relief that flooded through her show. Pest? Was that really all he saw in the gorgeous woman who obviously had her heart set on capturing his attentions?

With that assurance, she could afford to be generous. 'Oh, I think Eleanor means well,' she said. She paused for a moment. 'And she's obviously very fond of you,' she went on lightly. 'And Beth, too,' she added hurriedly.

'Possibly,' was the curt reply. Then he smiled. 'But even if that's true, it doesn't necessarily place me under any obligation to return the favour.'

'No-o,' she said slowly. 'Still, there's a lot to rec-ommend it.'

He shook his head. 'I don't know. Since my wife was killed, that kind of thing hasn't been high on my list of priorities. My work is very demanding, and with my concern over Beth——'

He broke off with a shrug, averting his eyes from her. After a moment he leaned his narrow hips back against the balustrade, folded his arms across his chest, crossed one leg over the other and gave her a quirky grin.

'You're very intent on matchmaking for me,' he said lightly. 'But what about you?'

'Oh, me,' she said with a wave of her hand. 'I'm far too busy to think of romance.'

He cocked a heavy dark eyebrow at her. 'Even with your doctor friend?'

'David has been just that—a friend,' she replied evenly. 'A good friend.'

'Ah, but how good? That day he came here to take you out he seemed to have something more than mere friendship on his mind.'

'Well, as you said yourself about Eleanor, that doesn't oblige me to feel the same way about him. We can't really call up our feelings to order, can we?'

'No,' he said with a slow shake of his head. 'I'm afraid we can't.'

He turned around, braced his elbows on top of the balustrade and gazed out at the sea. Neither spoke for several moments, but it wasn't an uneasy silence. In spite of their differences over Beth's therapy, which were only to be expected, she felt very much at ease with this man. There seemed to

be an unspoken rapport between them that didn't
need small talk to fill the gaps in conversation.

Finally he turned back to her. 'I don't mean to
be offensive, or intrude in any way, but can I ask
you a personal question?'

She smiled. 'Certainly. I don't have to answer if
I don't want to, after all.'

He leaned closer to her and peered down at her
face. 'I've noticed that you have some small faded
scars on your forehead. Not that they detract in the
slightest from your looks,' he added hastily.
'They're hardly noticeable. But I'm curious about
them. Beth tells me you were in an accident.'

From his opening sentence, fear began to clutch
at Sheila's heart. Did he suspect where the scars
came from? Who she really was? The part she'd
played in his own tragedy? Perhaps he'd already
found out. For a moment all she could do was stare
dumbly at him.

'Yes,' she replied shortly at last, looking away.
'But I'd rather not talk about it.'

'Of course,' was the quick reply. 'Sorry I mentioned it.'

'Not at all,' she said, grateful that he was backing
down so easily. 'Now, it's getting a little chilly. I
think I'll go inside.'

She turned to leave, but before she'd taken a step
away from him she felt his hand on her arm, heard
him speaking to her.

'Don't go,' he said in a low voice.

She turned around slowly to face him, and when
she saw the look on his face she almost gasped
aloud. His mouth was working with suppressed
emotion, a pulse beat furiously along the hard line

of his square jaw, and when their eyes met she instantly recognised the terrible hunger in those dark grey pools, a tacit appeal that touched her to her very core.

She caught her breath and put a hand at her throat, almost afraid of what was coming. As they stood there in silence for some moments, simply gazing wordlessly at each other, Sheila's face began to burn. For the life of her she couldn't make herself move a muscle or utter a word.

The tension continued to build up between them until it virtually crackled in the air, when suddenly, with no warning, she heard him mutter a curse under his breath and felt his hand tighten on her arm.

'Sheila,' he said in a low, throbbing voice, 'I've kept quiet and I've stayed away from you for as long as I can stand it. Now I've either got to say something, do something, or go out of my mind.'

'What . . . ?' she began.

But he reached out a hand and put one finger on her lips, silencing her. 'No,' he said softly. 'Let me finish.' He withdrew his hand and ran it over the back of his neck, staring with unseeing eyes off into the distance.

Then, with a little groaning noise deep in his throat, he reached out blindly for her, and the next thing she knew she was in his arms again, where she had longed to be, she now knew, during every moment of these past weeks.

Snaking her arms around his waist, she sank against him limply, and they stood there in a close embrace for a long time, not speaking, not moving. Finally, he drew his head back and put a hand under her chin, tilting her head up to face him, the grey eyes glittering down at her.

'You feel it, too,' he said with something like awe in his voice. 'I wasn't just dreaming.'

She shook her head, smiling. 'No,' she replied. 'You weren't dreaming. But...'

'No,' he whispered. 'Don't say anything. If I don't kiss you right now, I won't answer for the consequences.'

His dark head bent slowly towards her, and she closed her eyes, waiting, her heart pounding wildly. When his mouth settled firmly over hers at last, she sighed deeply and instinctively parted her lips so that he could deepen the kiss.

As his tongue darted inside her eager mouth, his hands began to move feverishly over her back, her shoulders, then, still clasping her around the waist, one hand moved upwards to cover her breast, gently at first, then with more urgency, moving from one to the other, as though to memorise each soft contour, each thrusting peak under her thin blouse.

Finally he raised his head and gazed down at her, his breath rasping, his eyes boring into her hotly. 'I've done my damnedest to stay away from you,' he ground out harshly. 'But I can't fight it another day.' He put his hands on her shoulders and smiled. 'I said once I thought you were a witch.'

Then his head bent lower, and she knew that if he kissed her again she'd be irrevocably lost. She turned her head away. There were so many things against it. If she was ever going to tell him her true identity, now was the time, before things got out of hand. She *was* powerfully attracted to him, and he'd been so open and honest with her that she owed it to him to be equally so.

'Sheila?' he said softly. 'What is it?'

She looked up at him. He was gazing at her, waiting for her response, the grey eyes glittering with desire, and her heart turned over. How could she tell him the whole story about the past now? There was no reason why he would ever find out, after all. Why not just let it go? Finally she decided to temporise.

She moved away from him. 'This is wrong, Ross,' she said. 'My first priority is Beth. I can't let anything interfere with that.'

'I agree. Don't you think I want what's best for her? Probably even more than you do, and I fail to see how pursuing our own relationship can possibly interfere with her welfare.'

'I can't give you a detailed blueprint. All I know is that it's asking for trouble to mix the personal and the professional.' She thought for a moment. 'Maybe if you were to find another therapist? There are several good ones I could recommend.'

'No,' he stated flatly. 'That wouldn't do. The progress you've made with her is remarkable. She's devoted to you, trusts you. To change therapists now would only set her back.'

Sheila bit her lip and stared out into the gathering dusk. He was right, of course. And although her concern about Beth was legitimate she knew that the real reason she was hesitating to take what Ross offered her was because of the past she was hiding from him.

Finally she turned back to him. He was leaning back on the railing, his arms crossed in front of him, his eyes upon her, waiting patiently for her to go on. She had to say something. Perhaps if she just touched on the past, tested the waters, so to speak, she might find the courage to go on.

'I loved my husband very much,' she began in a low, hesitant voice. 'When I lost him, I didn't think I'd ever be interested in any man, ever again.'

'And now?' he asked when she didn't go on.

'I don't know.' She laughed lightly. 'When you come right down to it, I hardly know you.'

'Then perhaps it's time we got better acquainted,' he said easily. 'I'm a patient man, Sheila. Let's just play it by ear and see what happens. You'll be here for some time, I imagine, working with Beth. I have another trial coming up in a few weeks, but in the meantime we can at least get to know each other better.'

But before she could make up her mind his hands were clutching her shoulders and his mouth had come down on hers again, a brief kiss this time, the merest feather-light touch of his lips.

'Think about it,' he said softly, releasing her. 'Why don't you sleep on it?'

'Yes,' she said. 'I will.'

Once again, she turned to go back to the house, but she'd only taken a few steps when she heard him call to her. 'One thing, Sheila.'

She turned to face him. 'Yes?'

'Whatever you—we—decide, I have no intention of sneaking around under my daughter's nose.'

'No,' she murmured. 'Of course not.'

He came walking slowly towards her, and when he reached her he stood looking down at her for a moment, then went on in a dead even tone, 'So I'd like you to consider spending a weekend with me at the apartment in the city. Soon.'

Startled at the unexpected request, and all that it implied, she widened her eyes at him and opened her mouth to object, but as though able to read her thoughts he held up a hand, stopping her.

'Just think about it, that's all I ask.'

During the next few days that was all Sheila *could* think about. She came up with a hundred reasons why she shouldn't do as he asked, and only one why she should—the simple fact that she wanted to, more than anything in the world. But that one reason was so compelling, so overpowering that in the end she knew she wouldn't be able to resist.

He didn't press her at all during that time, as though giving her plenty of room to think over his proposition without any pressure from him. Although she was grateful to him for that, she couldn't help wishing he hadn't put the decision entirely on her shoulders.

In spite of her confusion, however, those few days were the happiest she'd spent so far since she'd come to stay in his house, even though he still spent the bulk of his time in his study, where he was deeply absorbed in getting ready for his next trial, and they actually only saw each other when Mrs Swenson or Beth were also present, at meals or watching television in the evenings.

Although they behaved with complete circum-spection at all times, their relationship had altered dramatically, on a deep hidden level, and they seemed to be far more relaxed with each other, whether playing in the pool with Beth or watching one of her silly programmes.

Occasionally their eyes would meet, or they would touch inadvertently, and at those times the little shivers that ran up and down her spine, the warmth that flooded through her made her want to agree to anything he could ask of her.

Still, she did have her own work to do. After all, the reason she'd come here in the first place was to care for Beth. The girl had come a long way in a surprisingly short time, but there was still that all-important pain barrier to be hurdled.

On the following Wednesday morning, then, still no closer to a decision than she had been the night he'd proposed his weekend plan, she made up her mind to start the next stage of therapy that very day. It wouldn't be pleasant or easy, but it had to be done, and the sooner the better.

The four of them were just finishing breakfast. Sheila pushed back her chair, rose to her feet and glanced down at Beth with her brightest, most re-assuring smile.

'It's about time to get started on our morning session, Beth,' she said, holding out a hand. 'Shall we go? I'd like to try to take a giant step today, and it'll take a little more time than usual.'

'Oh, Sheila,' the girl said with a pleading look in her eyes. 'Mrs Swenson said I could help her make cookies after breakfast.'

Sheila sighed inwardly. She really was anxious to get started, but saying no to Beth now would only make what was coming harder. There was no real urgency. An hour or so's delay wouldn't make that much difference.

'All right,' she said, and was rewarded by a be-atific smile. Then she shook her finger at the girl with an expression of mock-sternness. 'But only for an hour, mind you.' She glanced at her watch. 'It's eight-thirty now. I'll expect you in the therapy-room at nine-thirty sharp. All right?'

Beth nodded her head eagerly. 'All right.'

'Promise?'

'Yes,' Beth replied solemnly. 'I promise.'

It wasn't until Sheila had turned and started towards the door that she realised Ross had risen from his own chair and was following her out of the kitchen.

'Sheila,' he called to her.

She turned around. 'Yes?'

'Since you've given Beth a recess, there's some-thing I'd like to discuss with you.' His tone was casual, but she could sense an underlying note of seriousness in it. 'Would you come to my study with me for a moment?'

'Of course.'

Out in the hallway they walked side by side towards his study. They didn't speak, didn't touch, didn't even look at each other, but she was so in-tensely aware of him that her whole body tingled with a pervasive warmth. She felt light-headed, and her heart was thudding erratically against her ribcage.

At the study door, he stepped aside, and as she preceded him into the room she gave him a swift glance out of the corner of her eye. His expression was grave, almost solemn, and a little thrill of ap-prehension shot through her. Was something wrong? Had she delayed too long?

When he followed her inside and shut the door behind him, she turned to him, her eyes questioning. But before she could utter a word he'd taken the one step that separated them and the next thing she knew his arms had come around her and gathered her closely up against his broad chest.

Almost sobbing with relief, she leaned her head on his shoulder and closed her eyes, hardly daring to breathe, lost in the sheer pleasure of his long, hard body pressed against hers, the strength of him, the delicious masculine scent.

His cheek came to rest on hers and he put his mouth at her ear. 'Oh, Sheila,' he murmured. 'You'll never know how often or how badly I've wanted to hold you like this these past few days.'

She turned her head slightly towards his, instinctively seeking his mouth, and in the next instant his lips claimed hers in a deep, satisfying kiss.

After a moment he drew his head back and loosened his hold on her. He put a hand under her chin, tilting her face up so that she was gazing straight into those glittering grey eyes. What she saw there almost took her breath away.

'I've kept my distance from you,' he began in a deep quiet voice. 'Left you entirely alone for three whole days.' He crooked his head to one side and gave her a rueful grin. 'Three hellish days, I might add,' he growled, raising his hands to her shoulders and giving her a little shake. 'Now, I've got to go up to San Francisco, and I'd like to have your answer before I leave.'

'When?' she asked quickly. 'Not right away?'

He continued to gaze down at her, his face stern now. 'I'm afraid so. Tonight, at the latest.'

Sheila's head whirled. What could she say? She wanted to go with him. But it had all happened so suddenly. She needed more time. She bit her lip and looked away from him.

'Today is Wednesday,' he went on in the same steady tone. 'I'd like to have you drive up on Friday. I'll arrange to keep the entire weekend free.' He put a hand on her cheek and gently forced her head around to face him again. 'Free to spend it with you,' he went on softly. 'Will you come?'

She gazed up at him with troubled eyes. She was about to hedge, to delay, to tell him she needed more time, but once again what she saw in those silvery depths melted all her resistance. All she knew was that she wanted to be with this man, at any time, any place, under any conditions.

Not trusting herself to speak, she only nodded.

'Is that a yes?' he asked, laughing.

'I—I guess so,' she heard herself croak. She cleared her throat. 'Yes. It's a yes. I'd like to come.'

Then his arms came around her again, and as he held her, his heart beating against hers, she knew she'd made the right decision. He had to care something about her. Of course he did. And she cared about him. More than that, she realised as his mouth sought hers again. In a sudden swift flash of insight she knew beyond a doubt that she was already hopelessly in love with this wonderful man and in danger of losing her head entirely if she wasn't careful.

With an effort of will, she pulled back from him and gave him a dead serious look. 'One thing, Ross.'

He grinned down at her. 'Anything.'

She had to smile. 'Be careful with promises like that. I might take you up on it.'

The smile faded and his face became grave. 'I mean it, Sheila. You must know how I feel about you. I know it's too soon for any commitments or long-range plans, but I've come to care for you deeply.' He put a hand on her face. 'You're not only a beautiful woman,' he said softly, 'but a caring one as well, a woman of integrity and purpose.' He grinned again. 'Who could ask for anything more?'

Sheila's heart sang. It was virtually a declaration of love. Certainly it meant some kind of future together. That made it all the more important to start out on the right footing. She'd tell him about the past this weekend, she promised herself. Surely it would be safe to do it then, when they were alone together at last.

Still, her innate caution warned her to slow down. 'There is just one more thing,' she said with mock-severity. 'I agree we need some time alone together, but I'm not quite ready for an affair.' She coloured slightly. 'Actually, since my husband died, there hasn't been anyone else. I need a little time.' She took a deep breath. 'So, I will come to spend the weekend in San Francisco with you, but I'll stay in my own apartment.'

His face fell immediately. He raised a hand to his chin, rubbing it thoughtfully, and stood there gazing out of the window for several seconds. Sheila held her breath, waiting for his response.

Finally he sighed and turned back to her. 'All right,' he said ruefully. 'Have it your way.' Then he brightened. 'But I won't promise not to try to seduce you.'

She laughed with sheer relief that she'd won her point. 'You can always try,' she rejoined. Then, deftly eluding his outstretched arms, she stepped away from him. 'Now, I have a date with your daughter and don't want to be late.'

He nodded. 'I should be ready to leave in an hour or so. I'll stop by on my way. Then I'll call you early Friday to firm up our plans.'

As she made her way to the room she used for Beth's therapy, Sheila's heart was singing. She hadn't a doubt in the world that she was doing the right thing by agreeing to meet Ross in San Francisco and spend the weekend with him. She'd feel safer in her own apartment, at least until she saw how things worked out with him once they were alone and out of his house where there were so many memories.

Alone with Ross! She could hardly believe it.

Beth was waiting for her, and at the sight of her small form huddled in the wheelchair an intense wave of tenderness for the girl swept over her. It was as though her love for Ross, knowing he returned it, at least to a degree, made her even more determined that the girl should walk again and live a normal life.

However, there would be a price to pay. She had to put aside her feelings for the father in order to do her best for the daughter. Unless she was able to push Beth past that fear of necessary pain, she would never walk again.

'All right, Beth,' she said briskly. 'Shall we get started?'

The girl eyed her warily. 'Will it hurt?'

Sheila knelt down beside the chair. 'Yes,' she said softly. 'There will be some pain. But you're going to be as brave as you possibly can, and keep thinking of the time when you'll be running and playing like other children.'

'But I don't want it to hurt,' the girl wailed, shrinking back from her.

'I know, darling, I know.' She thought for a minute. 'Remember I told you once that I'd been in an accident too?'

Beth nodded. 'I remember.'

'Well, I was in a wheelchair, too, and couldn't walk for a long time. And I'd still be in that wheelchair if a therapist a lot like me hadn't made me get out of it and start using my legs again.'

'Did it hurt?'

Sheila nodded. 'I'm afraid so.'

'Very bad?'

'At times, yes. But you know, Beth, it's a funny thing about pain. It's very unpleasant at the time, but when it's over you forget all about it.' She rose to her feet. 'Now, will you try your very hardest? I promise I'll stop if you really want me to. But when it hurts, just make a picture in your mind of that little girl running and playing.'

'All right,' Beth agreed reluctantly. 'I'll try.'

'Good girl. Now, you already can stand by yourself, and that's a big improvement over the way you were before.' She reached under the girl's arms and lifted her up out of the chair. 'We'll put you over here at the parallel bars to give you some support.'

She carried her over to the bars and very carefully set her down on her feet. Beth grasped hold
of the bars as though her life depended on it.

'That's great,' Sheila said. 'Now, let's take that
step, shall we? Come on, you can do it.'

Beth gingerly put one foot in front of the other,
then slowly, carefully, rested her weight on it, all
the while hanging on for dear life to the bars.

'Good,' Sheila encouraged her. 'You're doing
fine. Now, let go of the bars.'

Beth darted her a fearful look. 'I can't.'

'Yes, you can,' was the firm reply. 'You've done
it before. Come on, I want you to put all your
weight on your legs.'

Very cautiously, Beth did finally let go of the
bars. She gave Sheila a smile of triumph. 'I did it!'
she crowed.

'Yes, but you've done that before. Now take a
step without the bars. Just move that leg forward
and put your weight on it.'

Beth bit her lip and wrinkled her forehead in
concentration. Slowly, she dragged her other leg a
few inches forward and set the foot down on the
floor. At the contact, she uttered a little cry of pain,
started to sway and immediately grabbed hold of
the bars again.

'All right, Beth. Good try. Now again with the
other foot. Let go of the bars.'

'I can't,' the girl wailed, louder this time.

'Yes, you can. You can try.'

Tears were threatening by now, Beth's face contorted with fear. Sheila's heart went out to her, but
she knew she had to stand firm.

'Do it, Beth,' she said sternly. 'You managed with one foot, now try it with the other.'

'But it hurts!' was the tearful response.

'I know that, Beth, but I already explained——'

Just then a loud commanding voice boomed out behind her, chopping off her words, 'What the hell is going on here?'

Sheila whirled around to see Ross standing just inside the door. His face was ashen, drained of colour, his jaw clenched tight, his eyes blazing with fury. He began striding purposefully towards the bars, his arms outstretched for his daughter.

Sheila planted herself firmly in front of him, blocking his way, then squared her shoulders and put on her coldest, sternest expression. 'Ross, I want you to leave right now.'

'I'll be damned if I will!' he barked. 'Look at the child! She's terrified of you! What are you, some kind of sadist?'

'Ross, you've got to let me do this my way or not at all, and if you don't get out of here this minute I swear to you I'll pack my bags and leave. I mean it.'

Their eyes locked together in mortal combat for several long, tense seconds. Then, with a snarling sound deep in his throat, Ross turned on his heel and strode out of the room.

For a moment, Sheila couldn't move. Her heart was pounding in her chest, her face was on fire, and she was having trouble breathing. She squeezed her eyes tight shut, listening, terrified he'd come back.

But instead the next thing she heard was the sound of a car starting up out in the driveway, then

the squeal of tyres, the crunch of gravel, as it sped
away.

Well, she thought, there goes my great weekend.
Her shoulders slumped forward and she hung her
head. It seemed that every ounce of energy she pos-
sessed had drained out of her, and she was filled
with a sickening sense of dread.

Then she thought of Beth. She straightened up,
took a deep breath, put on a forced smile and
turned around.

'All right, Beth,' she said. 'Shall we try again?'

CHAPTER SEVEN

BY DINNERTIME that evening it had become clear to Sheila that her fears were well-grounded. She'd known in her heart that the weekend plans were off the moment she'd seen that look on Ross's face that morning, heard the fury in his voice.

Still, she couldn't help hoping, and when the telephone rang in the kitchen, just as she and Beth and Mrs Swenson were finishing their meal, her heart gave a great leap.

Mrs Swenson got up to answer it. 'Hello?' She listened for a moment. 'Oh, hello, Mr Calvert.'

Sheila clasped her hands tightly in her lap, exerting all her power of will to keep from jumping up and running to the telephone before she was summoned. He'd thought things over, she told herself happily, and had cooled off by now. He'd been so eager for their weekend together. He couldn't possibly have stayed angry for long.

She strained her ears, hoping to hear his voice on the other end of the line, her eyes fastened on Mrs Swenson, waiting for her to call her to the telephone. But all she could hear was an occasional muttered, 'Yes, sir,' or 'No, sir,' from the housekeeper.

When she finally set the receiver down on the counter, Sheila, all poised to get up, tried to catch her eye, but as though deliberately avoiding it Mrs Swenson turned to Beth.

'Here, honey. Your dad wants to talk to you.'

Sheila sank slowly down in her chair. She sat there numbly, listening to Beth speak to her father. The childish prattle seemed to be coming to her ears through a haze, as though from a great distance.

When Beth hung up, Sheila rose slowly from her chair. 'I'll help you clear away, Mrs Swenson,' she said dully.

'Oh, never mind about that,' she replied. 'Why don't you take Beth into the living-room? I'm sure there's a television programme she wants to watch right about now.'

The note of real sympathy in the woman's voice almost sent Sheila over the edge. As the hot tears began to smart behind her eyes, she quickly stopped them, struggling for control.

'Well, all right,' she said at last, forcing out a smile. 'If you're sure. Come on, Beth. What'll it be tonight?'

Luckily, Beth had one of her favourite cartoon programmes all picked out, so mindless that at least Sheila didn't have to pay attention to what was going on. She sat on the sofa next to Beth in the half-gloom, staring blindly at the flickering images on the screen, going over and over what had happened that morning—the confrontation with Ross, the way he'd challenged her authority, then stormed out when she'd stood firm.

Shortly after that furious interruption, she'd called a halt to the therapy session, but even so Beth had clearly made a major step forward that morning. She hadn't got very far, but at least she'd tried, and would have gone on trying if her over-protective father hadn't made that misguided attempt to rescue her.

She knew she'd done the right thing, for Beth's sake anyway, but that was cold comfort now as she saw all her dreams of a future with Ross Calvert go down the drain.

She closed her eyes and leaned her head back. It was probably all for the best anyway. She'd known from the beginning that the personal and the professional were a volatile combination. With Ross apparently out of the picture now she should be able to make even more progress with Beth, which was why she was here, after all.

Even so, late the next afternoon she decided she might as well pack her bag for the weekend, just in case. After sleeping on it, he could very well have got over his anger and perhaps would call her after all, as he'd said he would, to firm up their plans.

However, by dinnertime that evening there was still no word from him, and she had to face the fact that it really was all off, most likely for good.

She had just risen from the dinner-table after promising Beth to play a game of checkers with her after she'd had her bath, when the telephone did ring.

Once again Mrs Swenson answered it, then held it out to Sheila. 'Here. It's for you.'

Sheila rose slowly from her chair, and as she walked over to take the call a small spark of renewed hope rose up in her that she couldn't quite fight down. When she took the telephone from Mrs Swenson, she almost had to laugh at the way all her fine resolutions about the wisdom of putting an end to any personal connection with Ross had gone flying out the window so completely.

'Hello?' she said.

'Well, Sheila, it's been a while.'

Her heart sank. 'Oh, hello, David,' she said, lowering herself slowly down on the stool beside the counter. In the background she could hear Mrs Swenson wheeling Beth out to have her bath.

'My, such enthusiasm overwhelms me,' he said in a dry voice, only half joking.

'I'm sorry, David,' she assured him hurriedly. 'Guess I'm just tired. I've been working hard lately and have just reached a rather critical stage in Beth's therapy.'

'Well, that's one reason I called. I'm hoping I can talk you into coming up to San Francisco for the weekend. There's a big bash at the Fairmont hotel for the local branch of the American Medical Association, and I'd love to have you go with me. It's a rather posh affair. You know, white tie, formal dress.'

'Oh, David, I don't think——'

'Sheila,' he broke in firmly. 'I think you really do need a break. So does Kate. And it's been a long time since we've even seen each other. Come on, be a sport. Kate will be there, and a lot of your old friends.'

'I don't know, David,' she replied hesitantly. 'I really don't like to leave Beth right now.'

The minute the words were out of her mouth she knew she wasn't being honest, with David or with herself. After all, she had planned to spend the weekend in the city with Ross, and Beth hadn't stopped her then. Besides, it *was* the weekend. And after yesterday's sticky session it would probably be best to give the girl a rest anyway.

'Oh, come on, Sheila,' David was going on. 'Surely a few days won't set the therapy back.'

'You're right,' she said at last in a decisive tone. 'It won't hurt to leave her with Mrs Swenson for a day or two, and I guess I really could use a break right about now.'

'Wonderful!' David was jubilant. 'I'll pick you up tomorrow night at your apartment around seven o'clock. That should give you plenty of time to drive up here and settle in. Sound OK?'

'Yes. It sounds fine.'

'See you then.' He paused. 'And Sheila?'

'Yes.'

'Remember, it's formal, so bring your best finery.'

After they hung up she stood there with her hand on the receiver for several moments, deep in thought. After the fiasco with Ross, a night out with David and Kate, among her old friends from the hospital, was probably just what she needed. She'd been buried down here for far too long.

She'd leave tomorrow morning, right after breakfast. She was all packed and only had to choose something to wear to David's party. On second thoughts, she'd buy something new when she got to the city, have her hair done, perhaps even splash out on a manicure and facial.

It was a tremendous relief to be taking any action at all, planning something entirely on her own, without Ross's disturbing presence to consider. She'd fretted over it as much as she was going to. So far he'd called all the shots. Now it was her turn.

Still, as she lay in bed that night, going over her plans for next day's trip, a persistent image kept intruding into her thoughts, and the tall, dark man with the lean face and silvery eyes haunted even her dreams.

The next morning she announced her plans to Beth and Mrs Swenson at the breakfast table, and when she saw the look of relief on Beth's face she couldn't help smiling with amusement. Clearly the girl did need a break right about now as badly as she did.

'How long will you be gone?' Beth asked.

'Oh, just a few days.' She reached out to put a hand on the girl's shoulder and gave it an affectionate squeeze. 'But I'll be back, young lady,' she went on with mock-severity. 'And then we'll have to buckle down again to some hard work. Think of the weekend as a short recess. You've earned it.'

The girl glowed. 'Have I really?'

'Absolutely. You've been a very brave girl, and I'm convinced we'll have you walking again in no time now.'

Still glowing, Beth attacked her cereal bowl with gusto while Sheila finished her coffee and toast, still mulling over the last-minute things she needed to do to get ready for her trip.

'Sheila,' Beth said, pushing her empty bowl away. 'Will you see Daddy in the city?'

'Oh, no,' Sheila replied hurriedly. 'I plan to spend all my time with old friends.'

Mrs Swenson was coming back to the table with a fresh pot of coffee just then, and as Sheila glanced at her she could see that her round face was set in an expression of deep disgust.

'Men!' she muttered under her breath as she plumped herself down at the table. She gave Sheila a kinder look. 'You go on up to the city, honey, and have a wonderful time. You've earned it, too.' Then she glowered again. 'And not just for what you've done for Beth.' Then with a snort she poured out the coffee.

A few hours later, as she drove up the coast road towards the city, Sheila thought about that last little scene and had to laugh aloud. Apparently she'd found an ally in Ross's housekeeper, who seemed to know by a kind of osmosis just what had been going on. Wonderful how women can stick together in a pinch, she thought wryly.

It was just past noon when she arrived at her apartment building on Russian Hill, one of the older neighbourhoods in San Francisco. Although it was good to be in her own place again, when she let herself inside, it did seem rather cold and un-inviting. It even smelled musty, and the first thing she did was open a few windows to let in some fresh air. After a typical early morning fog, it had turned into a beautiful day, and the balmy breeze that blew off the bay soon cleared away the dank mustiness.

When she went into her bedroom to unpack, the first thing that caught her eye was the silver-framed photograph of Richard that still sat on her bedside table. Setting down her bag on top of the bed, she walked slowly around and picked up the picture, then stood there for some time gazing down at it.

It was almost like looking into the face of a stranger. It had been taken several years ago, before they were married, his college graduation picture, and he could only have been in his early twenties, just a boy, really.

Now those features, once so beloved, had dimmed so in her memory since his death that she could hardly recall what it was like to love him, to be his wife. They'd been happy during the short time they'd been married, but now, as her eyes glazed over, another face gradually began to super-impose itself on the photograph in her hand, older, more mature, with lines of suffering in it that were absent in the youthful features of her dead husband.

When she realised what was happening, she quickly set the photograph back on the table and got on with her unpacking. She had a lot to do that day and it was already one o'clock.

After wolfing down a scratch lunch of peanut butter and stale crackers and half a rather elderly apple, she set out on her shopping expedition. She'd made an appointment at one of the city's finest, and most expensive beauty salons for three o'clock for the full works, and wanted to shop for the new dress first.

It was good to be back on the city streets again, in spite of the smog, the traffic congestion and hordes of shoppers. She was really a city girl at heart, and it had been a long time since she'd en-joyed the pleasure of simply wandering around among the crowds, looking in shop windows and listening to the street musicians that seemed to be on every corner.

She loved San Francisco. As always, even in June, there was a slight coolness in the air from the breeze blowing off the bay, the familiar tangy scent of salt water wafted upon it, and she strode briskly towards her favourite dress shop on Geary Street.

An hour later, she emerged, dazed but triumphant, carrying her prize, the perfect dress, in the shop's distinctive silver and blue carrier bag. She just had time to make her appointment at the beauty salon, and for the next two hours she was washed and rinsed and blow-dried and cosseted, placing herself entirely in their hands.

By the time she let herself back into her apartment, she felt a bit dazed and light-headed, not only by the shopping and beauty treatments she'd undergone, but even more by the really horrendous amount of money she'd spent. It was already past five o'clock, just time for a long soak in a hot tub to wash away the grime of her afternoon's exertions before she got dressed.

She was all ready by quarter to seven, and gave herself one last dubious glance in the bedroom mirror before David showed up. He was due in fifteen minutes, and was always prompt. Even while she was putting on the new dress, she had begun to have second thoughts about it. What had looked so great on her in the shop now, with David's appearance imminent, seemed a little too daring.

Still, she decided, smoothing down the flared skirt and tugging at the tiny straps so that the bodice didn't reveal quite so much cleavage, it was flattering, a deep sea-green silk peau-de-soie, cut in a deep V, practically backless, and moulding her slim figure as though it had been made for her. A thin gold chain and a pair of loopy gold earrings completed the outfit.

She'd also had her hair done a new way, the thick, sun-bleached auburn strands piled high on top of her head, with two curly wisps hanging down in front of her ears, and, of course, the usual sweep of hair across her forehead to cover the remaining traces of her scars. Because of the revealing dress and rather flamboyant hairstyle, she had used very little make-up in an attempt to tone down the image a little.

The doorbell rang promptly at seven o'clock, and when she opened the door to David and saw the look on his face all her efforts were rewarded. His mouth fell open, his eyes glazed over, and he let out a low whistle as he stepped inside and closed the door behind him.

'God, Sheila, what have you done to yourself?'

'Well, quite a bit,' she replied with a self-conscious little laugh. 'Do you think it's overkill? Will I embarrass you in front of your doctor friends?'

'Lord, no,' he said with feeling. 'I'll be the envy of every other man there.' He cocked his head to one side and grinned at her. 'The only problem is, I may have trouble keeping my hands off you myself.' He shook his head. 'Really, Sheila, you've put some very dangerous ideas into my head.'

'Well, in that case maybe I should get out my grandmother's old cashmere shawl and drape it over my shoulders.' She frowned. 'Seriously, if you think it's too much...'

He held up a hand. 'It's perfect. I was only kidding. I know my place. Look but don't touch. At least let me enjoy the view. No harm in that. Now, shall we go?'

*   *   *

The party turned out to be great fun. It was held in the Cirque Room of the Fairmont hotel, which was filled to bursting, with everyone dressed in their best finery. As it turned out, Sheila's dress was a model of modesty compared to the creations some of the other women sported, and as soon as she saw the sea of female flesh they revealed she felt much more comfortable about her own appearance.

They sat at a table with Kate and her husband, who was a well-known psychiatrist, and another couple, a husband and wife team of cardiologists from the hospital. The dinner was at least edible, she managed to catch up on all the hospital gossip, danced until her feet ached in her high-heeled gold sandals, and by midnight was more than ready to call it a night.

David was unusually silent on the drive back to her apartment. A cautious driver in any circumstances, tonight he drove even more slowly than he normally did, and seemed so preoccupied that she had to wonder if he was annoyed with her about something.

'I really enjoyed myself this evening, David,' she said at last, just as he pulled up in front of her building. 'I hope you did, too.'

He switched off the engine and pulled on the handbrake, then turned to her. 'Yes, I did, except that——' He broke off.

'Except what?' she prompted.

He smiled at her. 'Well, you know, Sheila. It's the same old story.' He reached out a hand and placed it over hers. 'When are you going to let down that reserve of yours and give me a break? You know how I feel about you. In case you've forgotten, I love you. I want to marry you. Isn't there any hope at all?'

Sheila looked away, biting her lip. How simple her life would be if she were to marry David. Good, kind, safe David. She did *like* him a lot. In fact, eventually she probably would have ended up saying yes to his periodic proposals if only...

She stopped short. If only what? Immediately an image of the tall, dark man with silvery eyes flashed into her mind. But that was hopeless. If she were to agree to marry David now, tonight, it might put her safely beyond temptation where Ross Calvert was concerned. But would that really be fair to David?

Finally she turned back to him, her face troubled. 'David...' she began.

But he put a finger on her lips, stopping her. 'Never mind,' he said with a sigh. 'I know what's coming.' Then he brightened. 'Just so long as it isn't a flat no, I can live with it a while longer. Come on, I'll see you to your apartment.'

When they arrived at her door, she got out her key and unlocked it, then turned back to David. The corridor was always dimmed considerably after midnight, and his face was cast in shadows so that she couldn't quite make out his expression.

'I'd invite you in for a last drink, David, or a cup of coffee, but I've had such a long day that I think I'd really like to turn in now.'

'Sure,' he said. 'I understand.'

He bent his head down and brushed his mouth lightly over hers. While she responded as best she could, no bells rang, no sirens went off, no cold chills ran up and down her spine. He sensed that she was at least trying to enter into the spirit of the thing, and his arms came around her, pulling her up more tightly against him, and his mouth opened over hers.

Instinctively she froze and pulled away from him. With a long sigh, he dropped his hands. 'I'll let you go now,' he said. 'But you will think about what I said, won't you?'

'Of course, David,' she replied, meaning it. 'And I'm very flattered, you know that.' She put a hand lightly on his arm. 'You'd be a prize catch for any woman.'

'Could be,' he said with a little laugh. 'It just so happens, however, that you're the only woman I want.' He paused for a moment, but when she didn't respond he went on in a brisker tone, 'I'll call you tomorrow. I've arranged to take the day off. Maybe we can take a drive or something. How about it?'

'That sounds fine. Only don't call too early. I plan to sleep long and late.' She unlatched the door. 'Goodnight, then, David, and thanks again for a lovely evening.'

She stepped inside, flicked on the light and waved him a last goodbye. Then she stood there for a moment watching him as he moved away down the corridor towards the waiting lift. As the doors slid shut in front of him, she started to close her own door, when all of a sudden she heard footsteps from the far end of the hall, saw a looming figure coming towards her out of the shadows.

A sharp jab of fear shot through her. She put a hand at her throat and started to back inside, but when she looked again the figure had moved into the light, and she recognised it instantly as Ross Calvert, his face set, determination in every step he took. For a moment all she could do was stare.

'So,' he said, planting himself firmly in front of her, his arms crossed across his chest. 'You and the doctor are just good friends.'

'Ross!' she cried. 'What are you doing here? You scared me half to death!'

'Sorry if I frightened you,' he said. 'But I didn't want to interrupt the tender little love scene.'

'You—you heard?' she gasped. 'You mean to say you stood there listening all this time and didn't say a word? Of all the——'

'No,' he broke in. 'I wasn't eavesdropping, and I was too far away to hear what you and your doctor friend were saying. But I'd have to be blind and deaf not to get the drift.' He shrugged and gave himself a little shake. 'However, that's neither here nor there. I came because we need to talk.'

'Well, why didn't you call me? Or let us know you were here sooner? Why all this lurking around in shadows?'

He drew himself up to his full imposing height and looked down his nose at her. 'I was *not* lurking.' Then he grinned. 'Actually, I was afraid that if I called you you'd hang up on me, and that if I came knocking at your door you'd slam it in my face.'

She had to smile. 'I don't think I would have done either of those things.'

'Well, you probably had every right to. I behaved like a prize idiot the other day.' He paused a moment. 'Say, do you suppose we could go inside? Just for a minute. I have a few things I want to say to you.'

She hesitated for just a second, then opened the door wider to let him. 'All right. But just for a minute. I've danced my feet off tonight and these shoes are pinching in all the wrong places.'

'Why don't you take them off, then?' he asked reasonably as he followed her inside and closed the door behind him.

'I think I will,' she replied, slipping the sandals off her feet.

She started to take off her thin black summer coat, but when she remembered the dress she was wearing beneath it had second thoughts about displaying it in front of Ross. But she could hardly entertain him in her own apartment with her coat on.

At this point, however, what did it really matter? She removed the thin garment, hung it up in the coat cupboard, then turned back to him, fighting the strong temptation to cross her arms in front of her to cover the revealing dress.

However, after only one brief flickering glance, he marched directly over to the sofa by the window. 'Do you mind if I sit down?' he asked politely.

'No, of course not. Could I get you something? Coffee? A drink?'

He shook his head. 'No, thanks. As I said, this won't take long.'

He settled himself on the sofa, then sat there for a few moments, his long legs spread apart, elbows resting on his knees, hands clasped between them, staring down at the carpet. When Sheila passed in front of him to take the chair opposite, he glanced up at her, but didn't speak until she had sat down.

'First of all,' he began in a low voice, 'I know now I was wrong to create such a scene over Beth's therapy the other morning. I think I must have realised it at the time, but when I see her hurt I simply lose control. I'm just sorry you had to be the target. I know you're doing what's best for her, and I do trust your judgement.' He gave her a wry smile. 'The therapy-room should be off-limits to parents, I guess. Or am I your only hard case?'

Sheila laughed out loud. 'Oh, Ross, far from it! You wouldn't believe the lengths some parents will go to to protect their children from pain. Especially, I might add, fathers.'

'Yes, well, when it comes to the really important things, in general women do seem to have more backbone than men,' he admitted grudgingly.

'Could be. Anyway, believe me, yours is not a pathological case. It's only natural for you to want to protect Beth, especially when she's been through so much since the accident.'

'It's good of you to be so understanding,' he said stiffly. 'But what isn't so easily forgiven, I'm afraid, is the way I went storming out of the house in a rage and completely wrecked our weekend plans.'

'Yes, well,' she stammered, reddening. 'Perhaps that was all for the best in the long run, anyway.'

'No,' he stated firmly. 'Far from it. You'll never know how badly I wanted this weekend with you, how I was looking forward to it, and how I deeply regretted what had happened the minute I was out of the house.'

A little seed of anger had begun to sprout in her. *He* wanted the weekend badly! *He* was looking forward to it! *He* regretted it! And *he* was the one who'd ruined it!

'If that's true,' she said evenly at last, 'I wonder why you didn't see fit to call me and tell me.'

His eyes flew open. 'Well, I——' he sputtered. Then he shrugged. 'To be honest, I guess it just never occurred to me you'd come, after the way I behaved over Beth, the things I said.'

She gave him a withering look. 'Is that your opinion of me? That I'd hold a grudge against you for one outburst over Beth? Believe me, Ross, I've put up with much worse than that from indignant parents.' She shook her head. 'No, I think there's more to it than that.'

To her intense satisfaction, a deep red flush began to steal over his face, and once again he sat there staring broodingly down at the carpet. As she watched him, recognising his real distress, her heart went out to him and her anger began to leak away.

'What was the real reason, Ross?' she asked softly.

Without a word, he suddenly jumped to his feet and came striding over to her. For a long moment he simply stood before her, staring down at her, a look of supplication in the deep grey eyes. She couldn't turn away from them. They held her in their gaze almost against her will, and a slow warmth began to creep through her.

Then, wordlessly, he leaned over, bracing his hands on the arms of her chair, and the next thing she knew his mouth was pressing against hers. One arm came around her waist, pulling her up so that she stood before him, locked in his embrace, lost in the wonder of his kiss, the feel of his strong arms wrapped around her.

'Oh, God, Sheila,' he breathed, tearing his lips from hers. 'I was so afraid I'd lost you for good.'

She gazed up at him. 'Why, Ross?' she asked gently. 'I need to know. Why didn't you call me? You must have known I'd come.'

He shook his head. 'I'm not sure. I guess...' He looked away for a moment, and when he turned back to her his eyes were hard, his expression set. 'You probably don't realise this, but my marriage was not the idyll everyone thought it was.'

Of course she did know it. His own sister had spilled the beans long ago. But she couldn't tell him that. She knew how painful this must be for him, but he had to do it his way, without her help. She could only nod and wait for him to go on.

'I won't go into all the reasons for our troubles, but we ended by staying together only for Beth's sake. I'm quite sure she found her entertainment elsewhere, and, while I remained faithful in practice, whatever love I'd once felt for her died long before she was killed. As a consequence, I decided there would be no more heavy commitments in my future.' He shrugged. 'You know the saying once bitten, twice shy. I don't mean to imply that I've lived a celibate life. I've had a few meaningless flings, but the only things that had any real meaning for me were my work and my daughter. It seemed to be enough.' He paused for a moment, then gazed down into her eyes. 'That is, until you came along.'

Sheila's heart soared. Now, she thought. Now is the time to tell him the truth about the past, when he's being so open, making himself so naked, so vulnerable to me. Surely he'll understand. He won't blame me. The accident wasn't my fault.

She closed her eyes tight and turned her head away from him, in an agony of indecision, her head whirling. She knew he was waiting for her to say something, to make some response to the intimate details he'd just revealed to her. He was trusting her with his very soul, and he deserved the same from her.

By now her love for him had burgeoned into an exquisite tenderness that was actually physically painful. What was more, it seemed his own feelings for her ran much deeper than she'd imagined. Even if it was only an affair he wanted, it was obviously a serious one he had in mind. Still she hesitated.

'Sheila?' he said in a worried tone. 'What is it? Why don't you say something?'

She turned and walked away from him, clasping her hands in front of her, until she came to the window. Moving aside the curtains, she stared down at the street below, empty now of traffic at this late hour except for a few after-midnight stragglers. She knew she was only stalling for time, and that she owed him more than that. Unless she told him the truth, now, they couldn't go on. And she just couldn't seem to make herself do it.

Finally, she turned to face him. 'What is it you want from me, Ross?' she asked in a small voice.

'Good lord, woman!' he ground out. 'What do you think?'

In just three long strides, he came across the room and stopped just inches away from her. He stood there for a moment glaring down at her, virtually beside himself with sheer frustration, his brow like thunder, his silvery eyes narrowed into slits, his mouth working soundlessly.

Then, suddenly, he grabbed her by the shoulders, his fingers digging painfully into her flesh, and shook her so hard her teeth rattled. 'Damn it, Sheila,' he shouted. 'Haven't you heard a word I've been saying? I love you. I want you to marry me.'

CHAPTER EIGHT

SHEILA stared at him. In a split-second, all her hesitation simply vanished into thin air, and with a little cry she fell into his arms.

He held her to him for several moments in a soothing embrace, his hands stroking her gently, his lips in her hair. Finally his mouth moved to her ear, and the feel of his warm breath heightened the delicious sensations that were flooding through her.

'Am I to take that as a yes?' he murmured.

All she could do was nod. Ross loved her! He wanted to marry her! Stifling the nagging little pang of guilt over her silence and pushing it firmly to the back of her mind, she tossed caution to the winds and gave herself up mindlessly to the intense joy of the moment that filled her whole being.

She pulled her head back and smiled up at him. 'Yes! Of course it's a yes.'

'Well, then, you'd better kiss me.'

She threw her arms around his neck in a gesture of wild abandon, raking her fingers through the thick dark hair, and pressed her mouth against his. As his lips claimed hers, his hands began to move feverishly over her bare shoulders and back, then slid around to settle at the base of her throat.

Her heart was pounding so hard by now that he surely must feel it, she thought. His mouth opened wider over hers, his tongue seeking entry, and when the hand at her throat slid lower to cover her breast she drew in her breath sharply at the touch.

In the stillness of the room, broken only by the sound of his laboured breathing, the delicious tangy scent of the man, the feel of his hair under her fingers, the taste of his mouth on hers captivated all her senses. Pressing herself closely up against the hard length of his body, she became acutely aware of just how aroused he had become, and knew he felt it too.

With a low growl deep in his throat, he tore his lips away from hers. Gripping her by the shoulders, he held her slightly away from him, the grey eyes, almost black now with naked desire, boring into her.

'Are you sure you want this, Sheila?' he rasped hoarsely. Then the corners of his mouth quirked up in a wry smile. 'Because if you're not, we'd better stop right now, before it's too late.'

For reply, she reached out wordlessly and placed her hand on his cheek, stroking it over the light stubble on his jaw, and gazed deeply into his eyes.

'I love you, Ross,' she replied softly at last. 'And yes, I want you.'

'Oh, my darling,' he murmured. 'You'll never know how long I've waited for this.' His gleaming eyes dropped lower, flicking up and down her. 'I must say, that's some dress you're wearing.' Once again his lips curled in a crooked smile. 'Was that for the doctor's benefit?'

His tone was light, but the faint undercurrent running beneath it was serious enough to make her laugh. 'Oh, Ross, I do believe you're jealous.'

He gave her a stern look. 'Who, me? Jealous?' Then he sighed. 'All right. I admit it. I'm jealous as hell. Now tell me I have no reason to be.'

'None in the world, darling,' she said. 'David means nothing to me. I meant it when I told you we were only friends. You're the only one I want.'

He nodded with satisfaction. Then, his silvery eyes gleaming down at her, he reached out a hand, grasped one thin strap of her dress and slowly slid it down over her shoulder.

'I want to look at you,' he breathed, reaching for the other strap. 'All of you.'

She stood quite still, waiting, every sense alert, hardly daring to breathe, watching the expression on his face as his hands slid over her breasts, moving aside the thin wisps of silk that covered them. For several moments he stroked her in a gentle circular kneading motion, his fingers playing lightly about the throbbing peaks.

Sheila threw her head back and closed her eyes, giving herself up entirely to the exquisite sensations he was arousing in her. Her blood was on fire, and when she felt his hot, moist mouth on her shoulder she shuddered. Glancing down at the dark head moving towards her breast, she clasped it to her, cradling it in her arms.

Finally he raised his head, and began tearing at his own clothes, first shrugging off his jacket and dropping it on the floor, then his tie, but as he began to unbutton his shirt she reached out a hand, stopping him.

'Let me,' she whispered.

He dropped his hands to his sides and his eyes never left her as she unfastened each button in turn.

When she'd finished, she spread the openings of
his shirt apart and leaned over to place her lips on
his bare chest.

Suddenly she felt herself being swooped up in his
arms and being carried down the short hallway.
When they reached her bedroom he set her down
at the side of the bed, then knelt down before her
to pull her dress down over her hips, carrying her
tights along with it.

Once he had freed her of the last of her clothing,
he made his way back up slowly, inch by inch, his
hands and lips working their magic on her body,
first her ankles, then her calves, her knees, lingering
for a moment at her thighs, then travelling over her
abdomen and breast to settle on her mouth again.

He left her for a moment to remove the rest of
his own clothes, until he too was naked. She gazed
longingly at him, her eyes sweeping over the magnificent form, from the broad shoulders, over the
strongly muscled chest and flat abdomen, with its
narrow strip of coarse hair, down to his long
straight legs.

He reached for her and held her close for a long
moment, their bodies pressed together, then gently
eased her down on top of the bed. Bracing himself
on his elbows, he hovered over her, gazing down
into her eyes.

'I love you, Sheila,' he breathed. 'And I want
you. Now.'

'Oh, yes, darling,' she cried, throwing her arms
around his neck. 'Now.'

Slowly he lowered himself down and began the
slow dance of love, a rhythmic motion that
gradually built up to an almost frightening in-

tensity, until something seemed to explode inside her. She cried aloud as wave after wave rocked through her, and at last she felt him slump against her, exhausted.

The next morning, Sheila awoke early to a bright ray of summer sunshine streaming in through the bedroom window. She raised her head and blinked, then looked somewhat dazedly around at her surroundings. Then it dawned on her where she was—back in the bedroom of her own apartment.

At that moment, the long form lying next to her stirred and changed position. Memory came flooding back, and a great surge of warmth coursed through her. With a heart full of love, she smiled down at him. He was lying on his back, one arm raised over his head, still sleeping peacefully. The covers had slipped during the night and became tangled around his waist, revealing the sinewy muscles of his smooth chest and broad shoulders.

His dark hair was mussed, falling over his forehead, and there was a slight stubble of dark beard on his chin and jaw. The muscles of his face were relaxed in sleep, the strong features softened. Watching the steady rise and fall of his chest, Sheila caught her breath, transported by the sheer beauty of the naked man, even more breathtaking in the full light of day.

She squeezed her eyes shut and stretched widely, like a contented cat who'd just finished a bowl of cream, her mind and heart filled with recollections of the wonderful night she had spent in Ross's arms. This man loves me, she thought happily. He wants to marry me.

Then, suddenly, a large warm hand reached out for her, snaking around her waist and pulling her down. She settled herself against him, nestling her head in the crook of his shoulder.

'Well, good morning,' she murmured.

'Mm,' he murmured, nuzzling her hair. 'You smell good in the morning.'

He raised himself up on one elbow, propping his head in his hand, and gazed down at her through lazy eyes for a few moments, then his head came down to kiss her lightly on the mouth.

'And you taste good, too,' he murmured against her lips. He raised up again and smiled down at her. 'Do you love me as much this morning as you did last night?' he asked teasingly.

She wrinkled her forehead, as though deep in thought. 'I'm not sure,' she said in a serious voice. 'I'll have to think about it for a while.'

He threw back his head and laughed. 'Little devil!' he exclaimed, giving her shoulder a playful shake. 'Do I have to beat it out of you?'

'Oh, no, not that!' she cried. 'I give in. After careful consideration I've decided——'

She broke off, suddenly unable to speak. During the little byplay, his hand had come to settle on her midriff, and was now snaking up to outline the contours of her bare breasts, the long fingers scarcely touching her, moving in circles around and around, until she was melting with reawakened desire.

She reached up and twined her arms around his neck, gazing up at him with a long look of utter solemnity. 'More,' she whispered. 'I love you more this morning than I did last night.' Then she laughed. 'Now, does that satisfy your ego?'

'I'll think about it,' he replied. His mouth claimed hers again in a passionate, open-mouthed kiss, and he shifted to cover her body with his own.

Some time later, Sheila slid out of bed and padded barefoot into the bathroom to shower, leaving Ross sound asleep again, lying on his stomach, his arms outstretched, his head buried in the pillow, just like a child.

When she was finished, she pinned her damp hair up on top of her head, put on a robe and came back into the bedroom. By now Ross was awake, sitting up in bed, his knees pulled up, and was holding out a hand to her.

'Come and sit down for a minute,' he said.

'Ross!' she exclaimed. 'You're insatiable!'

He laughed. 'No. Not that. Honestly, I just want to talk. We have to make some plans.'

'How about if I fix us some breakfast first?'

He shook his head. 'Later.'

She sat down beside him and put her hand on his knees. 'What do you want to talk about?'

'Well, I thought we might——'

He broke off abruptly, and his eyes narrowed in a puzzled frown. He peered closely into her face, which was totally bare of make-up after her shower, examining it carefully. Then he reached out a hand and ran one finger along her hairline.

'Those scars,' he said. 'You never did really tell me how you got them.'

An impending sense of dread clutched at her heart. 'Do they bother you?' she asked lightly.

'Of course not,' he assured her hurriedly. 'They're hardly noticeable.' He withdrew his hand and leaned his head back on the pillow. 'You said once you didn't like to talk about the accident that caused them,' he went on. 'But you'll have to admit that a lot of important things have changed since then. I want to know everything about you.'

Sheila took a deep breath. She had to do it now. Nothing could have been more clear. Gathering all her courage, she searched her mind for just the right words even to begin, when the sudden jangling of the telephone in the hall broke the silence.

She jumped up, clapping her hand to her forehead. 'Oh, lord!' she exclaimed. 'That must be David. He said he'd call me this morning.'

'Don't answer it,' Ross said promptly, reaching for her hand.

She glanced down at him to see that his face was creased in a frown of annoyance. 'Oh, Ross, I have to.' She paused for a moment. 'We—um—we had a sort of date for today.'

'You're not going to keep it, I hope,' he said in stern tones.

'No, of course not,' she replied, pulling her hand away. 'But I do have to talk to him, to explain. He knows I'm here. If I don't answer, he'll just keep calling, then get worried and probably come barging over to make sure I'm all right.'

Before he could protest further, she made a dash for the door. She ran to the telephone and snatched it up on what was at least the seventh ring.

'Hello.'

'Good morning,' came David's pleasant voice. 'All rested up?'

'Oh, yes.'

'Well, what do you want to do today?'

'David,' she began hesitantly, 'I'm afraid something has come up and I won't be able to see you today.'

'Oh, really? Nothing serious, I hope.'

'Well, it is rather.' There was no way out of it; she had to tell him. 'You see,' she went on, 'Ross Calvert is in town, and I promised I'd spend some time with him today.'

'But you already had a date with me,' he protested mildly. 'That's not like you, Sheila.'

'Well, to tell you the truth, there's more to it than a simple date.' She paused for a moment, then plunged ahead. 'In fact, we're going to be married.'

There was dead silence on the line. From the bathroom she could hear the shower turning on, and in spite of her concern over David's reaction to her announcement an immediate unbidden image flashed into her mind of the warm spray splashing on that tall, strong body under the shower. She closed her eyes as a wave of desire went through her.

Finally David spoke. 'I see,' he said quietly. 'Well, I guess there's nothing much for me to say.' He gave a dry laugh. 'At the moment, I'm afraid I can't really offer you my congratulations.'

'I'm sorry, David, but you know yourself that I've always been open with you about my feelings. I never made you a single promise, or did one thing to make you believe I ever considered you anything but a good friend.'

'I know that,' he replied with a sigh of resignation. 'I'll let you go now. We'll talk again later.'

After they'd hung up, she walked slowly into the kitchen to put the coffee on. She was sorry about hurting David's feelings, but she was determined not to feel guilty about him. He had no claim on her whatsoever, and she'd never lied to him.

Not the way she had to Ross, she thought with a sudden twisting sensation in the pit of her stomach. But withholding the truth wasn't really the same thing as a lie, and she had been just about to tell him when David called. Now the moment had passed.

As she set the coffee on to percolate, she remembered that there wasn't a single thing to eat in the apartment except peanut butter. She'd have to run out to the corner grocery store to pick up some eggs and bacon, bread, of course, and oranges for juice.

When she went back into the bedroom to get dressed, Ross was standing over by the window. He'd obviously just come out of the bathroom, fresh from his shower, a towel wrapped around his waist, his dark hair wet, and the sight of him filled her with an overwhelming need to touch him.

Smiling, she began to walk towards him, but when she saw that he was staring fixedly down at the photograph of Richard the smile faded and her heart lurched sickeningly. His photograph had been in the newspapers at the time of the accident.

He looked up as she approached him. 'Is this the husband?' he asked, picking up the silver frame.

She nodded. 'Yes. That's Richard.'

He looked at it again, examining it more closely. 'A nice-looking fellow. It must have been taken some time ago.' He gave her a teasing grin. 'He looks much too young for you.'

She smiled tentatively at him. 'Well, it was taken years ago. It was his college graduation picture.'

Suddenly he frowned. 'You know, there's something about him that looks awfully familiar, but I just can't think where our paths could have crossed. Of course, as you say, it's an old photograph. He must have changed somewhat by the time he died.'

'Yes,' she said shortly. 'Now, if we're going to have any breakfast, I have to go to the store to replenish my food supply.'

It was a beautiful day, warm and sunny, and after breakfast they decided to go for a drive up into the Napa Valley to visit some of the famous wineries there.

They stopped by Ross's apartment first so that he could change his clothes. To her surprise, there was nothing opulent about it, at least compared to his lovely home in Monterey. Apparently he just used it as a *pied-à-terre*, a place to sleep in, when he was in the city working on a case. There were only two rooms, a small living-room and even smaller bedroom, with a bath and small kitchen alcove. It was all sparsely furnished in nondescript motel style, with no personal amenities at all that she could see.

It only took a few minutes for Ross to dress. While she waited for him in the living-room, she leafed idly through the morning paper, but without any real interest. The little scene over Richard's photograph still disturbed her. She should have told him then, but somehow it hadn't seemed like the right moment.

She had to ask herself then if that moment would actually ever come. In fact, by now she had pretty much decided that there was actually no reason to tell him at all. It was ancient history, after all. It had nothing to do with their future life together. Of course there was always the danger that he'd find out on his own somehow, but who was there to tell him? No one knew but Kate and David, and she was certain neither of them would ever mention it.

And even if he did find out, would it really matter? Ross was a reasonable man, an experienced, worldly man. He would never blame her for something that was actually Richard's fault. So what was the point in dragging up an old issue that was totally irrelevant to their life today?

Still, she couldn't quite fight down the nagging, insistent little voice deep inside her that kept asking why, if it was such an unimportant issue, she didn't just come out with it now.

Just then, Ross reappeared. He was wearing a pair of dark trousers and a white shirt open at the neck, the sleeves rolled up to reveal his strong forearms, with their silky mat of dark hair, and everything else was forgotten at the sight of him. Those finely chiselled lips and large strong hands had worshipped her body during the night, and she wasn't going to allow anything to take that away from her.

'Shall we go?' he asked, coming over to her chair and holding out a hand.

She jumped to her feet and took his hand. 'All set,' she replied, smiling happily up at him.

He bent his head to kiss her lightly on the mouth. 'Then let's be on our way.'

It was a heavenly day, the sun beating down constantly as they drove along, and the further they travelled north-east, into the interior of the valley, the hotter it became. Sheila was wearing a white sundress with a matching jacket, and by the time they reached the small city of Santa Rosa had shed the jacket and was still uncomfortably warm.

'Shall I turn on the air-conditioning?' Ross asked.

'Oh, no. I quite enjoy the breeze. The air is so much fresher here than it is in the city. But I am getting a little hungry. How about you?'

'Yes, I could use something to eat. I know a little place here in town that serves wonderful Italian food. How about it?'

He grinned at her, his strong white teeth flashing against his tan skin. Her heart melted, and she couldn't resist putting out a hand to run it along his bare arm, the silky black hairs so smooth under her hand. She could feel the muscles in his arms tighten at the touch, and he gave her a wry look.

'Watch it, lady,' he warned. 'Keep that up and we may never eat again.'

Quickly she removed her hand, and folded both hands in her lap. 'Sorry about that.'

'Oh, don't be. We'll take up later where we left off.'

The restaurant had a large paved patio in the back, shaded by a gigantic old oak tree. There were tubs of bright red geraniums scattered around, and the scent of roses was heavy on the warm summer air. Since it was past one o'clock when they arrived, they had the place almost to themselves, and took their time over a long, leisurely lunch of pasta smothered in a rich tomato sauce and one of the local dry red wines.

After he'd finished eating, Ross leaned back in his chair, taking a sip of his wine. 'This is great country, isn't it? In fact, I've always had it in the back of my mind to buy a small place up here to retire to one day. Nothing very grand, just a small vineyard and a garden to putter around in.'

'Why, Ross!' she exclaimed. 'I would never have thought of you as a farmer. Your home is so beautiful. Wouldn't you miss the ocean?'

'Oh, I suppose. But I must have farmers' blood in my veins. My people came from here, you know—at least, my grandparents. I've always been sorry my father sold the old homestead before he died.'

'Both your parents are dead, then?' she asked.

He nodded, then leaned forward across the table, put a hand over hers and gave her a searching look. 'How about you?' he asked. 'You've never mentioned your family. Are any of them around to pass judgement on your future husband?'

She shook her head. 'Afraid not. I'm an only child, no brothers or sisters, and my parents were rather elderly when I was born. A mid-life surprise! They died some years ago.'

'That's too bad,' he said. He turned her hand over and raised the palm to his lips. 'But now you'll have a family again. Beth adores you, Jane and Howard heartily approve. And then,' he added, gazing into her eyes, 'there's always me.'

Happiness bubbled up within her, creating a choking sensation in her throat. 'Yes,' she breathed huskily. 'There's always you.'

He released her hand and leaned back again, eyeing her carefully. 'Well, what do you think of my idea? Would you mind terribly leaving the city, the ocean?'

'Of course not. Not if it could be with you,' she replied softly. Then she laughed. 'Of course, that's a long way in the future. We have plenty of time before you think about retiring. And right now I have my own work to do.'

'Yes, but I like to plan ahead. An aspect of the legal mentality, I guess. But I agree. So long as we're together, it doesn't really matter where we live, does it?' He rose to his feet. 'Are you ready to leave?'

She got up beside him, smoothing down her skirt, and took him by the arm. 'All set.'

'I have a few details to wind up in preparation for my trial that I really should take care of this afternoon,' he said once he'd paid the bill and they were walking out to the car. 'So I think I'd better drop you off at your place when we get back to the city. Then I'll pick you up around seven and we'll go out for a late dinner. How does Fisherman's Wharf sound? Or is that too touristy?'

'No. I love seafood. That sounds great.'

As usual Fisherman's Wharf was full of the usual throng of sightseers, especially on a Saturday night, but Sheila didn't mind the jostling crowds. The pungent aroma of fresh fish and salt water tideflats seemed stronger than usual because of the warm weather, but she didn't mind that, either. Nothing could have disturbed her euphoric mood, wandering around the city she loved, hand in hand with the man she adored.

'I made reservations at Mario's,' he said, pointing at the tiny restaurant perched just ahead at the end of the pier. 'It doesn't look like much, and the décor is straight out of the shores of Sicily, but the scampi is out of this world. But perhaps you've already been there?'

'No, I never have. But I've heard about it for years and always wanted to try it. And I love scampi.'

'Then, let's give it a whirl.'

The fishy smell was even stronger inside the tiny restaurant, and was now mingled with garlic and spices. There was a thick layer of sawdust on the floor, and jammed into the dining-room were ten tables, all of them occupied. They were covered with red checked tablecloths, with squat candles set in the centre of each.

'What do you think?' Ross asked with a rueful glance at the crowded dining-room. 'Shall we find another place or wait?'

'Oh, let's wait.' She glanced inside. 'I think a couple in the back are just getting ready to leave.'

As she watched the departing couple make their way towards the foyer, it seemed to Sheila that they looked vaguely familiar, but she couldn't quite place them. It wasn't until she came face to face with the woman that she knew who she was, apparently just at the same moment that she recognised Sheila.

'Why, Sheila Fulton!' the woman exclaimed. 'As I live and breathe!' She turned to her male companion. 'Look who's here, Ted. It's Sheila Fulton.'

'Hello, Marian, Ted,' Sheila said, holding out a hand. 'It's been a long time.'

'Oh, simply ages!' Marian went on. 'Ever since your wedding, in fact, and that must be at least two years ago. Ted got posted to Paris right after you and Richard got married, and we've been out of the country ever since. Just got back last week, in fact.' She lowered her voice and squeezed Sheila's hand. 'We were so sorry to hear about Richard's death. A tragic accident. He was so young, so full of life.'

'Yes,' Sheila murmured, withdrawing her hand.

In the shock of seeing her old friends, she had forgotten for a moment that Ross was standing behind her. Now she saw Marian's gaze shift past her, and she had no choice but to introduce them.

When she turned to him, his eyes were sweeping over her friends with an odd, somewhat puzzled expression in them, as though something about them troubled him.

'I'd like you to meet Ross Calvert,' she said. 'Ross, this is Marian and Ted Wilson, old college friends of mine.'

Just then, to her intense relief, she saw the hostess beckoning to them. 'Oh, I think our table is ready,' she said hurriedly. 'We'd better grab it before she gives it to someone else. It was nice to see you again, Marian, Ted.'

'Give us a call,' Marian said as they started out of the door. 'We're in the book.'

When they were gone, Sheila darted another swift glance over her shoulder at Ross. His drawn face seemed drained of colour, and he was holding himself stiffly, as though suppressing some violent emotion. There was a closed-in expression on his face. His mouth was set in a firm line, his jaw clamped shut.

Whatever it was that was bothering him seemed to go more deeply than she'd realised, but it wasn't until the hostess had seated them at their table and she was able to study him more closely that she became seriously alarmed. He seemed utterly stunned.

'Ross?' she said, reaching out a hand across the table. 'What is it? Is something wrong?'

For a long moment, he simply stared at her, his deep grey eyes dazed, searching her face, as though trying to discover the answer to a riddle there.

'That woman,' he finally said in a low voice. 'Your friend, Marian.'

'Yes?' she asked, still puzzled. 'What about her?'

'She called you Sheila Fulton.'

Then it hit her. Of course. Marian had no way of knowing she'd gone back to using her maiden name after Richard's death, so had naturally called her Sheila Fulton. And Ross, of course, knew her as Sheila Waring.

Her head began to whirl. The photograph Ross thought he recognised! The scars from the accident she wouldn't talk about! He must have put it all together!

'Ross,' she began in a pleading voice, clutching at his hand in sheer desperation.

But he jerked his hand away, silencing her, then sat there staring wordlessly at her, an expression of loathing on his face. A little pulse was pounding at his jaw, and his brow was like thunder.

'Just who the hell are you, Sheila?' he muttered harshly at last.

CHAPTER NINE

SHEILA couldn't answer him. What could she say? The chance encounter with her old friends had left her totally unprepared. She'd been so sure it would never crop up, and now, just by the merest coincidence, here it was, staring her in the face, and she'd have to deal with it. The only trouble was that for the life of her she couldn't think how.

She knew instantly, of course, that it was too late—far too late—to pretend she didn't know what he was talking about. All she could do now was try to make him understand.

'Ross,' she said again, holding out a hand to him.

He jumped to his feet. 'I've got to get out of here,' he muttered hoarsely.

He turned on his heel and stalked away from her, winding swiftly around the closely packed tables, almost bumping into a waiter with a loaded tray. She stared after him blankly for a moment, dazed at his abrupt departure, then got up to follow him.

Outside, he marched down the street to the car, oblivious of the crowds, his eyes fastened straight ahead, moving so fast that she had to run to keep up with him. When he reached it he made straight for the driver's side. Panting, she arrived just in time to open her own door and slip inside as he started the engine.

That drive seemed like the longest twenty minutes of her life. Although his movements were jerky and there was some grinding of gears, Ross was too good a driver to take chances, even in his agitated state of mind. It was the dead silence that was so hard to take. He stared grimly ahead, his jaw clamped together, and she knew it would be futile to utter a word.

Eventually he slid into a space in front of her apartment building and slammed on the brakes. Immediately, with the motor still running, he reached across in front of her to open her door. She turned and gave him a hesitant look.

'Aren't you coming up?' she asked in a small voice.

'What do you think?' he snarled.

'Ross, we've got to talk. You have to give me a chance to explain why I didn't tell you sooner who I really was.'

He jerked his head around and gave her a long contemptuous look. 'I don't *have* to do anything,' he stated flatly. 'Not where you're concerned.'

'Ross, you're not being fair.'

'Fair!' he shouted. 'You accuse me of not being fair, when you've constantly lied to me for months now? I *trusted* you, Sheila, trusted you absolutely, with my home, my daughter——' His voice broke and he looked away. 'My whole future was wrapped up in you.'

She reached out to put a hand tentatively on his arm, and when he didn't shrug it off she found the courage to go on. 'Ross, I know how you must feel. Finding out that I was in the car that caused the accident has been a terrible shock to you. But I wasn't driving that car. And I suffered from it, too.

I have the scars to prove it. You can't blame me
for something I didn't do.'

He turned to her again, his eyes wild, wide and
staring. 'Is that what you think?' he demanded
angrily. 'That I blame you for the accident?' He
gave a harsh laugh. 'What do you take me for?
Why would I do that?'

'Then why. . . ?' she began in a bewildered voice.

'You tell me why!' he shouted. 'Why didn't you
tell me about it yourself? You must have recognised me. As I recall, we did run into each other
at the hospital, and *my* face wasn't covered in bandages at the time. You should have told me the truth
the moment you set foot in my house. Yet you went
on deceiving me for months, even after——' He
broke off, waving a futile hand in the air.

There was nothing she could say. He was right,
of course. It wasn't the accident he blamed her for.
It was the fact that she'd been less than honest with
him. Still, she had to try.

'I wanted to tell you,' she said in a low voice. 'I
even started to tell you several times, but something always seemed to interfere. Or perhaps I was
just too cowardly. Then, when you told me you
loved me, wanted to marry me, I was afraid that
if you found out it might make a difference to how
you felt.'

'Well, I did find out, didn't I?' he said in a low,
menacing voice. 'And believe me, lady, it makes a
big difference.'

'Ross, don't you understand?' she cried. 'I was
afraid of losing you. . .'

'Get one thing straight, Sheila,' he said in a dead
even voice. 'I had enough female deception in my

marriage to last a lifetime. I don't need any more from you. Now, if you don't mind, I'd like to get out of here before I do something we'll both be sorry for.'

It was no use. Her only hope was that after he got over the first shock and calmed down he'd be able to forgive her. He did love her, did want her, of that she was certain. At least he had, before this happened.

Without another word, she opened her car door and got out. He waited at the kerb until she'd let herself inside, then, with a squeal of tyres and grinding of gears, shot off down the street.

It was a terrible night. After pacing around the apartment like a caged animal, she fell into bed early, then lay there tossing and turning, half the time cursing herself for her cowardly procrastination, the other half cursing Ross for his pig-headed refusal even to try to see her side of it.

But most of all she missed him. It was astonishing to her how quickly she'd become accustomed to his loving, attentive presence in her bed, her heart, her very life, and without him the apartment seemed cold and dismal.

Although she couldn't help hoping, by the next afternoon, when he still hadn't called, she knew it was hopeless. On several occasions the temptation to call him was so overwhelming that she actually found herself at the telephone, her hand on the receiver, her heart pounding, before she came to her senses and dropped it. What would be the point of risking another rejection? It would only make her more miserable than she already was.

Around two o'clock that afternoon she made herself a late lunch of scrambled eggs, the only food in the house, bought yesterday morning for Ross's breakfast. Although it tasted like cardboard, she did feel marginally better with something in her stomach. She hadn't eaten a bite since their lunch yesterday in Santa Rosa.

Tears filled her eyes as she recalled every detail of that glorious day and the heavenly night that had preceded it. It had all been so perfect, until . . .

'Now, stop that!' she said aloud. She wiped her eyes and blew her nose on her paper napkin, then poured herself a cup of coffee and stood at the kitchen window, staring down blankly at the street below, the occasional car passing by, a few joggers.

She had to decide what to do now, and it came to her immediately that her first commitment was to Beth. If Ross intended to fire her, it was up to him to let her know, and until he did she'd better get on with the job she'd been hired to do. Beth expected her to return this evening, and that was what she would do.

After all, she thought as she repacked her bag, losing Ross wasn't the end of the world. It only seemed like it.

Sheila was deeply touched by the surprisingly warm reception she received from Beth when she arrived back at Ross's house early that evening. It went a long way to easing the ache in her heart.

It was just past six o'clock, and the minute she parked her car in the drive Beth shot out of the house in her chair, her face alight with pleasure.

'Sheila! Sheila!' she called, racing towards her across the front porch, and finally coming to a screeching halt just at the edge of the top step.

'Hey,' Sheila called back, hurrying to her side. 'Take it easy, young lady. That's a good way to send yourself toppling over the stairs.' Grasping the arms of the chair, she leaned over to give the girl a swift peck on the cheek.

To her astonishment, Beth immediately threw her arms around her neck. Although Sheila had always believed the girl was fond of her, she was basically a reserved child, and such an eager open-hearted demonstration of affection came as a complete surprise, especially after their recent painful therapy sessions.

'You came back!' Beth cried happily.

Gently disentangling herself from the stranglehold the girl had around her neck, Sheila smiled down at her. 'Of course I came back, silly. I said I would, didn't I?'

She glanced up just then to see Mrs Swenson emerging from the house. Her arms were folded across her ample bosom, her expression grim. For a moment Sheila had the awful feeling that somehow the woman knew exactly what had happened in San Francisco, even though she knew that was ridiculous. Or, worse, perhaps Ross had already delegated the job of firing her to the housekeeper.

But as she came closer Sheila could see that the stern mouth was twitching a little at the corners, and she was shaking her head and rolling her eyes in mock-indignation.

'That girl!' she said, pointing at Beth. 'She's been hanging at the window all day waiting for you to get home. I told her not to expect you until this evening, but she paid no attention to me.'

Sheila laughed with sheer relief. 'Well, I'm here now. And I hope I've made it in time for dinner. I'm starved.'

That wasn't quite true, since her stomach was still tied up in knots, but she knew it would please Mrs Swenson, and she really should eat something.

Mrs Swenson nodded with satisfaction. 'Good. I've got a nice roast in the oven. It should be done in half an hour.'

'Sounds great,' Sheila said. 'That'll give me time to clean up first. I feel pretty grimy after that hot drive. I'll just get my bag from the car.'

Half an hour later, showered and dressed in a light cotton skirt and blouse, Sheila made her way to the kitchen. Beth was already seated at the table, and Mrs Swenson was at the counter slicing the roast.

During her drive down from the city, Sheila had gone over and over the events of the weekend in her mind, and had got exactly nowhere, except to confirm her original conviction that she must continue her work with Beth at all costs.

Not only would it be a welcome distraction from her own shattered hopes, but she felt that helping Beth walk again somehow might make up for the fact that it was her own husband who had caused the accident that had put her in that wheelchair and taken her mother from her.

In order to do that, she had to put her personal feelings for Ross on hold. She also had to have Beth's full confidence. The warm welcome she'd just received from her went a long way towards assuring her that she had that trust.

'It smells delicious in here,' she said as she took her place at the table next to Beth.

'Not much you can do to a good roast beef,' Mrs Swenson declared, setting down a platter on the table and taking her own chair. 'Now, let's start, shall we?'

It was very pleasant in the large airy kitchen, just the three of them sharing a meal. Mrs Swenson had pulled the blinds down at the window to shield the room from the sun, and a light ocean breeze blew in through the open door.

Sheila found she had more appetite than she'd realised, and was actually enjoying the meal, listening with only half an ear to Beth's usual chatter about her television programmes, until suddenly she heard the girl ask her a direct question.

'Did you see Daddy in the city?'

Sheila's heart skipped a beat, and she stopped short, her fork halfway to her mouth. Her head came up abruptly, and she found herself gazing directly into Mrs Swenson's blue eyes. She flushed and looked away, but not before she'd seen the look of compassion on the woman's face.

'Now, Beth,' Mrs Swenson said. 'What makes you think Sheila would see your father? San Francisco is a huge city, and I'm sure she wanted to spend her time with her old friends.'

'Yes,' Sheila said hurriedly. 'It was good to see them again.'

She went on to describe the party she'd gone to with David on Friday night, and was relieved to see that Beth was so interested in all the details that the painful subject was forgotten.

The next few weeks were difficult, but rewarding as well. After careful consideration, Sheila had decided to take a more oblique approach with Beth's therapy. Ross's obstructive interruption to their last session had undone a lot of the progress they'd made, and with him apparently out of the picture now she would have the chance to repair some of the damage.

Although she wasn't actually starting out from scratch again, she did believe it was wiser for now to lead up to the more painful aspects with caution. Consequently, each day she pushed the girl a little further, but slowly, and by the end of two weeks they were at least up to the point they'd reached before.

In fact, they'd made such good progress that when Kate called to say she was coming down for a short visit that Sunday Sheila gave Beth the day off. It wouldn't hurt anything, and she was anxious to discuss the situation with her old friend.

They had lunch at a small restaurant in Monterey, and during the meal she filled Kate in on the progress she'd made with Beth.

'Sounds great to me,' Kate said when she'd finished. 'I think you're going about it in exactly the right way. What's your next step?'

Sheila made a wry face. 'Well, I just don't see any way out of trying to get past that pain barrier again.'

Kate nodded. 'I agree. It has to be done. From what you've told me, I think she's ready.' She hesitated for a moment, then went on in a halting voice. 'Sheila, David told me about your—well, your plans. You know, with Ross Calvert. But you haven't even mentioned his name today, and I can't help wondering why.'

'Oh, Kate, it was awful. I can hardly bear to talk about it, even now.' She bit her lip and looked away, then turned back to her friend with a sigh. 'You were right, you know. I should have told him about Richard. He did find out.' She told her about running into her old friends that night at Fisherman's Wharf.

'And he was furious, I take it.'

Sheila rolled her eyes. 'Oh, yes. Believe me, he was furious. And with good reason. It wasn't the fact that I was involved in the accident that sent him over the edge, but that I hadn't told him about it.'

Kate nodded. 'Yes. I was afraid of that. Well, what are you going to do about it?'

Sheila gave a helpless shrug. 'There's nothing I can do. It's over. At least he hasn't fired me. In fact, I haven't heard a word from him for the past two weeks. He calls Beth almost every night, but never asks to speak to me. When I get her walking again, which I hope will be soon, I'll just quietly disappear.'

'Huh!' Kate snorted. 'That doesn't sound like the Sheila Waring I know, the girl who came back practically from the dead to walk and work and live again.'

Sheila smiled wanly. 'Yes, but that was different. I had help, of course, from you and David mostly, but basically it was something I knew I had to do

on my own. However, I'm afraid no amount of will-
power can force another person to love you. It takes
two to make a love-affair, you know.'

'Yes,' Kate agreed grimly. 'I'm afraid it does.'

The next day was Mrs Swenson's day off, and Sheila
and Beth had the house to themselves. It was a
perfect opportunity to push Beth over that last
hurdle. By now she was able to stand alone again
and take a few steps with the parallel bars to support
her weight. Now it was time to do it without that
support, and it wasn't going to be pleasant.

'Well, Beth,' she said with a cheerful smile.
'Today I think we're going to start walking.'

As usual, the girl was waiting for her by the
window in the therapy-room, and although the look
she gave Sheila was apprehensive there was also an
indication of her own determination in the set of
her jaw, the steady grey eyes. At that moment she
looked so like her father that Sheila's heart turned
over.

'So, let's get started, shall we?' Sheila said, going
to her and wheeling her over to the bars. 'Just do
what you've been doing. Come on, I'll help you.
Up out of the chair and hang on to the bars; that's
the way.'

For the next hour they worked steadily, but
seemed to get nowhere, no matter how hard Beth
tried. Sheila had counted on getting Beth to take
those first steps on her own, believed she was ready
for it, and the failure was a great disappointment.

It certainly wasn't for lack of trying. Over and
over again, Beth would let go of the bars and try
to put her weight on her own legs, to take that

crucial step, but each time she would wince with
pain and grab on to the bars again. By now there
were tears in the girl's eyes, her face was contorted
with the heroic efforts she was making, and Sheila
knew it was time to quit.

'All right, Beth,' she said, walking towards her
with her arms outstretched. 'I think that's enough
for today. Don't worry about it, darling,' she said
when she saw the girl's face fall. She put an arm
around her shoulders. 'You tried your best, and
that's all anyone can ask. I'm more certain than
ever now that you'll do it eventually. It'll just take
a little more time.'

Beth gave a loud sniffle, and gazed up at her.
'Do you really think so?' she asked tearfully.

'Of course I do,' Sheila stated firmly, giving her
a reassuring pat on the cheek.

'Then maybe I'll try one more time.'

'Oh, I don't know, Beth. I think you've probably
had enough for today.'

'Just once more,' she begged.

'All right. One more try, then I'll fix us some
lunch and you can rest up this afternoon.'

She stepped back a few paces and stood, chin in
hand, her mind focused so intently on the little girl
that she didn't even realise there was someone
standing in the hall just outside the door until a
brief movement caught her eye.

Without turning her head, she darted a sideways
glance in that direction. When she saw Ross
standing there, it simply took her breath away, and
she almost gasped aloud.

Although her knees felt weak at the sight of him,
her first instinctive thought was for Beth. On no

account must he enter that room! As far as she could tell, Beth hadn't seen him, and she prayed he'd stay well out of the line of her vision while she made this one last valiant effort.

Their eyes met briefly, then she turned her gaze quickly back to Beth. All she could do now was hope that the look she'd given him was warning enough for him to stay out of sight. For now, she had to give all her attention to Beth.

She had pulled herself along on the bars, and had just let them go to stand alone. She was biting her lower lip hard, her face screwed up with determination, but still stood there hesitating. As usual, the minute she tried to take that first step alone, her first instinct was to grab hold of the bars again, and it looked like the same old story, another failure.

Then, just as Sheila was about to call a halt, the miracle happened. Beth had let go of the bars again and taken her first tottering step, putting all her weight on her own feet. At the painful impact, she uttered a little cry, and Sheila's eyes flicked briefly at Ross again.

He was still standing there, silent and rigid as a statue, and at the sound of his daughter's cry a look of anguish appeared on his face. He raised a hand helplessly in the air, but to Sheila's intense relief he didn't utter a word or take a step.

Turning immediately back to Beth, ready to congratulate her and call it quits for the day, Sheila was astounded to see that the girl was taking another step unaided. Then she took another, and another, until finally, exhausted, she reached the end of the bars.

Although the tears were streaming down her face by now, she was laughing at the same time. 'I did it, Sheila!' she cried triumphantly. 'I did it! Did you see me? I walked all by myself.'

'Of course I saw you, darling,' Sheila said, rushing to the girl's side and gathering her to her. 'I'm so proud of you.' She turned her head to see Ross walking slowly towards them, and as he came closer she could see the tears glistening in the grey depths of his eyes.

She turned back to Beth. 'Look, Beth,' she said. 'Here's someone else who saw you walk.'

As Beth looked past her to see Ross, she gave a loud glad cry. 'Daddy! Did you see me? I walked, I walked!'

'Yes, darling,' he said hoarsely. 'I saw you.'

He knelt down then and held his arms wide, and Beth stumbled towards him. With the tears smarting behind her own eyes at the heart-piercing sight that father and daughter made, Sheila began to back slowly and quietly out of the room.

Her job was done. Now that Beth had taken those crucial first steps, the rest would all be downhill, and another therapist could easily take over.

It was time for her to leave.

It was with mingled joy and sorrow that Sheila packed her bags that afternoon. Although she was thrilled that Beth was able to walk again, and even more so that her father had witnessed her first steps, it had caused her more pain than she'd anticipated to see him again.

At the time, her entire attention had been directed at Beth, but now, recalling those few brief

glances she'd had of him, it seemed to her that he'd
looked very tired, even rather gaunt, his face drawn,
his eyes dull. But that might have been from the
stress of standing by and watching Beth suffer. At
least he *had* stood by.

She'd heard the car drive off shortly after she'd
left the therapy-room, and assumed that Ross had
taken Beth out to celebrate. After making herself
a quick lunch, she'd gone through the silent house
to her own room. The sooner she left, the sooner
she could put it all behind her.

When she'd finished packing, she sat down at
the desk in her room to write a letter of resignation
to Ross, an affectionate note to Beth, and her best
wishes—and gratitude—to Mrs Swenson. When
she'd finished, she sealed them in envelopes and
put them on the kitchen counter, where they'd be
sure to find them.

By five o'clock, she was ready to leave. She gave
her room one last glance to make sure she'd tidied
away every trace of her occupancy, then picked up
her two heaviest bags and carried them out to the
car.

She had just raised the boot lid and started to
stow them inside when she heard a car come up the
drive. She turned around to see Ross just emerging
from the driver's side. He was alone. There was no
sign of Beth.

She stood there for a moment, one arm raised to
shade her eyes from the lowering sun, watching as
he walked slowly towards her. He did look tired,
and her heart went out to him. Without a word,
she turned quickly to shove the suitcases further
back inside the boot and shut the lid.

'What do you think you're doing?' she heard him ask in a low voice behind her.

She turned slowly around. 'I'm leaving.'

'Why?'

'It's obvious, isn't it? Beth doesn't need me any more.'

He raised a hand in the air, then let it drop to his side. 'But I do,' he stated simply.

'Oh, Ross,' she said in a weary voice. 'Let's not kid ourselves. You made it perfectly clear how you felt about me that last night in the city. You'll always hold what I did against me. Please don't start it all up again. I couldn't bear it.'

When she heard the catch in her voice, she swiftly averted her head. Oh, why did he have to come back this way, just when she'd worked up the courage to get out of his house, out of his life? Now it would only be that much harder.

She started to move away from him, but before she'd gone a step she felt his hands on her shoulders, stopping her. Squeezing her eyes shut tight, she stood there, unable to move, waiting. She just wanted to get this over with and leave.

'Sheila,' she heard him mutter. 'Turn around. Please. Look at me.'

Something about the pleading note in his voice touched her, in spite of her resolve, and she slowly turned around. When she looked up at him she saw that she hadn't been mistaken earlier. His face was haggard, the high cheekbones prominent, the creases at the corners of his eyes etched more deeply.

'God, how I've missed you!' he breathed, and with a low groan he reached out and gathered her into his arms.

She didn't have the strength to resist him, and, in spite of everything that had gone before, neither could she fight down the hope that rose within her. It felt so wonderful to be back in his arms again that all she could do was lay her head on his shoulder, close her eyes, and give herself up to the joy of the moment.

'Come on,' he said, after a moment. 'Let's go into the house. We need to talk.'

'But where's Beth?' she asked.

'Oh, I drove her up to Jane's house, and they insisted on keeping her for the night to celebrate.'

With his arm around her, holding her closely up against his side, they walked silently up the path and went inside to the living-room. Taking her by the hand, he led her over to the couch and they sat down side by side.

'There's so much to say, I hardly know where to begin,' he said at last with a rueful smile. 'I guess the best place to start is to tell you that I've been a prize idiot, that I've behaved abominably to you, and ask you to forgive me.'

Sheila's eyes widened in disbelief. 'Forgive you! But I was the one who...'

He put a finger on her lips, stopping her. 'Oh, I'll admit it would have been better all around if you'd told me from the beginning who you really were. Running into your old friends was a hell of a way to find out, and it knocked me for a loop. I felt as though I'd just been punched hard in the stomach.' He shook his head. 'But that still doesn't excuse my own actions.'

'Ross, I can hardly blame you for being angry with me. I knew all along I should tell you. I even started to several times. But at first it really didn't seem to be necessary, then, later, I was terrified I'd lose you.'

He waved a hand in the air. 'As far as I'm concerned, that's all water under the bridge now. If you can forgive me for my behaviour, I certainly can forget that you were slightly less than honest with me over one thing.'

Still she hesitated. She had to be sure before she could risk loving him again. 'But Ross, you were so angry with me,' she said at last. 'Do you really believe you can forget?'

He opened his mouth, then shut it again and looked away, frowning. To her surprise, when he turned his gaze back to her, his face was flushed, and there was a distinctly sheepish expression on it.

'About that,' he said in a clipped voice. 'To be perfectly honest with you, and after giving it a lot of soul-searching thought during these past few weeks, I've had to face the fact that an important aspect of my anger at you was my own guilt.'

Her eyes widened at that. '*Your* guilt?'

'Oh, yes,' he replied grimly. 'Remember, I was driving the other car, and although the accident wasn't actually my fault it did kill the woman I no longer loved, had even come to resent.' He smiled. 'I think any psychiatrist would tell you that guilt is a pretty predictable reaction to a situation like that, especially when it's not admitted. So I blamed you.'

He gave her a rueful smile. 'Anyway, the important thing is that I can't seem to function without you.' A spark appeared in his silvery eyes. 'I love you, Sheila. And I want more than anything to marry you, if you'll still have me.'

Have him! With a glad little cry, she reached out for him blindly. His arms came around her, holding her tightly. A hand came under her chin, tilting her head up, and as their eyes met the dark head came down to cover her mouth with his own.

The moment she felt those warm, sensual lips on hers, all rational thought left her, and her only desire was to surrender totally to this man. Fire licked through her as the gentle pressure hardened, became more demanding. Her lips parted to allow his thrusting tongue entry, and they clung together, tasting and savouring each other at the feast of love.

His hands moved possessively over her back, along her waist and hips, and then up over her ribcage to settle on her breasts, already aching for his touch.

His head came up and he raised his hands to cradle her face, the long fingers tracing her features. 'Do you know what?' he muttered. 'You've got too many clothes on.'

She smiled. 'I do believe you're right. What shall we do about it?'

For answer, he reached out and, with his glittering grey eyes never leaving hers, slowly began to unbutton her blouse, until the last one was undone and he slid the blouse off her shoulders and over her arms.

She sat motionless before him, watching as his gaze drank in her bare shoulders, the wispy flesh-coloured bra, the smooth flesh above the waistband of her skirt. He raised his hands to run them lightly over her breasts, back and forth, until the ache became more than she could bear.

'Oh, Ross, please,' she choked, her eyes pleading.

He smiled and reached around to undo the clasp of her bra. As he pulled the straps down over her arms, his hands brushed against the burning naked flesh, and she closed her eyes in an agony of longing.

'You're so beautiful, darling,' he murmured.

Finally, she could bear the sweet torment no longer. She reached out and began to tug at the knit shirt he was wearing, pulling it over his head, then running her own hands down from his broad shoulders, over his chest and flat stomach. He trembled under the touch, his muscles and sinews rippling under the smooth skin.

He stood up then and held out his arms. She rose to her feet, and with their arms around each other, not speaking a word, they walked slowly together towards her bedroom.

Dusk was beginning to fall by now, and her room was cast in shadows. Still, as they removed what remained of their clothing, there was enough light to see each other.

Slowly, they sank together down on the bed, and Ross's hands and mouth began to work their magic on her, raising her to such a pitch of desire that she finally had to cry out.

'Now, Ross! Oh, please, now!'

'Yes, darling,' she heard him groan, and they were joined together once again. As they rode the crest of the wave together, Sheila clung tightly to the man she loved, tumbling headlong over the precipice with him, ready to go wherever he led her, any time, any place, for the rest of her life.

Look out for Temptation's bright, new, stylish covers...

They're Terrifically Tempting!

We're sure you'll love the new raspberry-coloured Temptation books—our brand new look from December.

Temptation romances are still as passionate and fun-loving as ever and they're on sale now!

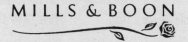

MILLS & BOON

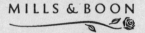

Cruel Legacy

One man's untimely death deprives a wife of her husband, robs a man of his job and offers someone else the chance of a lifetime...

Suicide — the only way out for Andrew Ryecart, facing crippling debt. An end to his troubles, but for those he leaves behind the problems are just beginning, as the repercussions of this most desperate of acts reach out and touch the lives of six different people — changing them forever.

Special large-format paperback edition

OCTOBER
£8.99

W●RLDWIDE

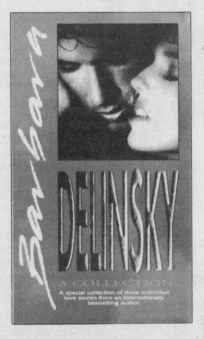

Next Month's Romances

Each month you can choose from a wide variety of romance with Mills & Boon. Below are the new titles to look out for next month, why not ask either Mills & Boon Reader Service or your Newsagent to reserve you a copy of the titles you want to buy – just tick the titles you would like and either post to Reader Service or take it to any Newsagent and ask them to order your books.

Please save me the following titles: Please tick

		✓
TRIAL BY MARRIAGE	*Lindsay Armstrong*	
ONE FATEFUL SUMMER	*Margaret Way*	
WAR OF LOVE	*Carole Mortimer*	
A SECRET INFATUATION	*Betty Neels*	
ANGELS DO HAVE WINGS	*Helen Brooks*	
MOONSHADOW MAN	*Jessica Hart*	
SWEET DESIRE	*Rosemary Badger*	
NO TIES	*Rosemary Gibson*	
A PHYSICAL AFFAIR	*Lynsey Stevens*	
TRIAL IN THE SUN	*Kay Thorpe*	
IT STARTED WITH A KISS	*Mary Lyons*	
A BURNING PASSION	*Cathy Williams*	
GAMES LOVERS PLAY	*Rosemary Carter*	
HOT NOVEMBER	*Ann Charlton*	
DANGEROUS DISCOVERY	*Laura Martin*	
THE UNEXPECTED LANDLORD	*Leigh Michaels*	

If you would like to order these books in addition to your regular subscription from Mills & Boon Reader Service please send £1.90 per title to: Mills & Boon Reader Service, Freepost, P.O. Box 236, Croydon, Surrey, CR9 9EL, quote your Subscriber No:.................................. (if applicable) and complete the name and address details below. Alternatively, these books are available from many local Newsagents including W H Smith, J Menzies, Martins and other paperback stockists from 13 January 1995.

Name:..

Address:...

................................Post Code:.........................

To Retailer: If you would like to stock M&B books please contact your regular book/magazine wholesaler for details.

You may be mailed with offers from other reputable companies as a result of this application. If you would rather not take advantage of these opportunities please tick box.   ☐